THE
REVELATION
of
JESUS CHRIST
CLEAR
AND
UNDERSTANDABLE

Gary Alan Rothhaar

Copyright © 2012 by Gary Alan Rothhaar.

Library of Congress Control Number: 2012904164
ISBN: Hardcover   978-1-4691-7955-1
               Softcover   978-1-4691-7954-4
               Ebook   978-1-4691-7956-8

All rights reserved. No part of this book may be reproduced or transmitted in any form or by any means, electronic or mechanical, including photocopying, recording, or by any information storage and retrieval system, without permission in writing from the copyright owner.

This book was printed in the United States of America.

To order additional copies of this book, contact:
Xlibris Corporation
1-888-795-4274
www.Xlibris.com
Orders@Xlibris.com
113196

DEDICATION

I dedicate this publication to my Lord and Savior Jesus Christ for He is the one who forgave my sins, saved my soul, indwelled me with the Holy Spirit, revealed His word to me, and inspired the writings of this book. I would also like to thank my faithful friends Jeff and Tami Eldridge, Patrick Bevier, and my son Jason Rothhaar for their valuable support and advice during the writing of this book.

Gary Alan Rothhaar

PREFACE

While studying this presentation of Revelation, please have your bible at hand so that you can read each verse and be familiar with its content before reading the related comments.

Gary would also encourage you to open all references that are **not** italicized because they will shed valuable light on the subject matter.

Gary does not expect all readers to agree with everything written in this book. He only asks that readers complete the book and keep an open mind to all of the biblical concepts that are presented. This book contains more than 500 biblical references to verify its scriptural accuracy.

Table of Contents

Book of Revelation   Brief Overview   *by Gary Alan Rothhaar*..............1

Part One, First 3 ½ Years of Seven (Tribulation)

Rev.	Chapter 1	John commissioned to write	11
Rev.	Chapter 2	Letters to Churches	13
Rev.	Chapter 3	Letters to the Churches	17
Rev.	Chapter 4	John's Vision of Heaven	21
Rev.	Chapter 5	The Book with 7 Seals	25
Matt.	Chapter 24	The Mt. Olivet Discourse	27
Daniel	Chapter 9, 11	Why, Seven Years of Tribulation?	31
Rev.	Chapter 6	Six of Seven Seals opened	35
Rev.	Chapter 7	The 144,000 Sealed	41
Rev.	Chapter 10	The Edible Book	45
Rev.	Chapter 11	Two Witnesses	47
Rev.	Chapter 12	The Woman (Israel)	55
Rev.	Chapter 13	Antichrist (beast) Revealed	61
Rev.	Chapter 14	The "Wave" Offering,	71

Part Two, Second 3 ½ Years of Seven (The Wrath of God)

Rev.	Chapter 8	Seventh Seal Opened Seven Trumpets Sound	87
Rev.	Chapter 9	Demons from bottomless pit, and Euphrates River	91
Rev.	Chapter 15	Prelude to Seven Bowls Judgment	95
Rev.	Chapter 16	Seven Bowls Judgment Undiluted Wrath of God	97
Rev.	Chapter 17	Mystery Babylon	105
Rev.	Chapter 18	The Fall of Babylon	113
Rev.	Chapter 19	Marriage Supper of the Lamb	117
Rev.	Chapter 20	Satan Arrested and Imprisoned 1000 years	123
Matt.		Jesus Separates the Sheep from the Goats	127
Rev.	Chapter 21	The New Heaven, New Earth, and New Jerusalem	139
Rev.	Chapter 22	The River and Tree of Life	147

TWO PARTS of the 7 years of tribulation.

Included in the book of the Revelation of Jesus Christ is a seven year period of time when a series of terrible events will occur worldwide. The purpose of the seven years of tribulation is to awaken the Jewish people as to whom their true Messiah is.

Since the Jews have rejected Jesus as their true Messiah, Romans 11:7, 8 says, "God has caused them to have a spirit of slumber." In other words, they are spiritually asleep, while God's Spirit of Grace is spread abroad to the Gentiles. Israel needs to be awakened so they can see and understand that their true Messiah is Jesus Christ, and they can still accept Him even now, just as we can by simply believing in Him as our personal Savior.

This presentation of Revelation is divided into two parts.

PART ONE

The first 3 ½ years of the 7 years of tribulations is basically the wrath of Satan poured out on all who oppose his new world order. The new world order is an evil world system designed to destroy all opposition, and ultimately exalt Satan through his "right hand man", (the antichrist), as king of all kingdoms of this world. He will be a counterfeit to Jesus Christ, "King of Kings, and Lord of Lords."

PART TWO

The second 3 ½ years of the great tribulation will be God pouring out His wrath on the kingdoms of the antichrist, and the unrepentant reprobates who have rebelled against God and harmed or destroyed His people throughout history.

The second part will also include the establishment of a peaceful earthly kingdom where Jesus Christ will rule and reign with His saints for 1000 years, followed by a new heaven, new earth, and a new Jerusalem where believing saints (as the bride of Christ) will live forever.

This book is designed to study all chapters that pertain to the first 3 ½ years, and then all chapters pertaining to the last 3 ½ years. The idea of doing it this way is to offer a better understanding of the sequence of events.

Book of Revelation   Brief Overview   *by Gary Alan Rothhaar*

All believers know that God is Good, and Holy, and Righteous, and True, and Perfect in all His ways.

But God has an enemy called Satan who is just the opposite, and there is no good in him at all. He is out to steal God's creation from Him so that he can have all the glory for himself.

The book of Revelation is about a major war between God and Satan. God is out to save as many people as possible, especially His chosen people, the Jews. But Satan is out to destroy God's chosen people.

The Jews are God's chosen people because God chose their blood line, beginning with Abraham, Isaac, and Jacob, to bring the Messiah, or Savior into the world. That Savior is Jesus Christ.

Jesus did come to earth through the blood line of the Jews as a baby in a stable at Bethlehem. He grew up and lived a perfect, sinless life and He preached about the kingdom of God. He tried to save as many people as possible. All they needed to do to be saved was to believe in Jesus; that He is their Messiah.

But when He came to deliver them from sin and oppression, and to set up His Kingdom on earth, they did not recognize Him as their Messiah because they were looking for a military leader. So they demanded that He be crucified as an imposter.

He was rejected by the Jews, and crucified by the Roman soldiers, dead and buried, but since Jesus is God the Son, He has the power to lay His life down and take it up again. On the third day He arose from the dead, and He ascended back to heaven.

Now the Jews are still waiting for their Messiah to come and deliver them from sin and oppression. When actually He has already been here and they rejected Him.

Because they rejected Him, Romans 11:7-8 says, "God has caused them to have a spirit of slumber", in other words, they are spiritually asleep, while God's Spirit of Grace is spread abroad to the Gentiles. Israel needs to be awakened so they can see and understand that their real Messiah is Jesus, and they can still accept Him even now, just as we can by simply believing in Him as our personal Savior.

So God is still trying to win the Jews back to Him even though they have rejected Him. God will never ever give up on His chosen people. But the Jews are a stubborn, stiff necked people. They won't wake up without a major event happening to them.

That major event is called the great tribulation. It is a seven year period of time when terrible things will happen on this earth. All of these terrible events are designed to awaken the Jews and to punish the people who have hated God and tried to destroy His people.

So the book of Revelations is about the war that is taking place between God and Satan. (Good and evil)

God will try to awaken the Jews and win them to His side, while Satan just wants to destroy Jews and Christians so that God's promises can not be fulfilled and God becomes a liar like Satan is. God's main promise to the Jewish people in the Old Testament is, Ezekiel 37: 27 someday God's tabernacle shall be with them and He will be their God and they shall be His people. But, that isn't happening right now because they have rejected their Messiah.

Since the Jews have rejected Jesus as their Messiah they are still waiting for a Messiah to come to them, and that is a great opportunity for Satan to send a false messiah to deceive them. That false messiah will be the antichrist.

The antichrist will foster a seven year peace treaty between the Arabs and the Jews that will guarantee the Jews protection, but in the middle of those seven years, as soon as they finish building their temple, he will break the treaty and try to destroy them. *Dan.9:27*

The antichrist will hijack the newly built temple and sit in the temple proclaiming himself to be God (II Thess.2: 4), at that time the Jews will wake up and realize he is a deceiver and Jesus is their true Messiah.

The Jews will then flee for their lives and scatter to get away from him and his armed forces. Satan will spend the rest of his time and energy trying to locate and destroy the Jewish people. Satan will go to any extreme to thwart God's plans for Israel.

Yes, Satan is that evil, and it is that important to him to destroy the Jews and make God a liar. Believers know that Satan could never make God a liar but it's Satan's only hope of avoiding God's judgment for him which is the lake of fire where he will be tormented day and night forever. Rev.20:10. The "lake of fire" is Satan's worst fear.

But God will somehow protect the Jews from the antichrist even while they are scattered. *Rev.12:13-14*

God will also protect us, not so much from the troubles of that time because the antichrist will even target us as Christians, but God will not subject us to the anger that He will bring on those who are trying to harm His people. **How will He protect us?**

He will be with believers during these times of trouble which are mainly the first 3 ½ years. Then when the antichrist breaks the peace treaty with the Jews in the middle of the 7 years and tries to destroy them, God will intervene and call His people out of the world to be with Him, not only the living, but also those faithful people who have passed on before His return. I Thess.4:16, 17

He will rapture (rescue them) and change their mortal bodies into spiritual bodies that will never die, and we will forever be with the Lord. I Corin.15:51-55

Then God will proceed to pour out His undiluted wrath on the wicked people of the earth who have blasphemed His name. Blasphemy means to knowingly reject God, even with cursing.

So the last 3 ½ years of tribulation will be far worse than the first 3 ½, but believers won't be here for that because we will be with the Lord.

At the end of the 7 years of tribulation there will be a final battle called Armageddon which God will win, of course.

Then Satan will be subdued and Jesus will set up His kingdom on earth which is called the millennium. The millennium is 1000 years of peace and tranquility. Everyone will get along just fine because Satan is bound and he can't bother anybody.

After the 1000 years Satan will be released for a short time. Again he will try to rally multi-national forces to attack Israel but God will defeat them and throw him into the lake of fire were he will be tormented day and night forever. *Rev.20:10*

But God's people will forever be with Him in a wonderful place called Heaven, the New Jerusalem, or the City that is Built Four Square.

The question is: When will all this take place?

No one except God knows exactly when but there are signs of the times that tell us it could be soon, even within our life time.

Here are some things that might happen as we get closer to the days of tribulation.

There will be many imposters pretending to be Christ.
There will be wars and starvation and disease in many places of the world.
There will be high crime waves and the love of many will grow cold.

The antichrist will rise in power and seem like a good person. He will have lots of good ideas for these times of trouble. He will be a powerful world statesman and make a peace treaty between the Jews and the Arabs for 7 years, but then he will break the treaty and try to destroy the Jews.

Someone will try to assassinate the antichrist but when it looks like he is dead he will survive a terrible head wound and people will think he is "supernatural."

After he survives the assassination attempt, possibly by an overly zealous so called Christian, he will begin to persecute the saints of God. Many of the lukewarm church people will be so afraid of him that they will betray true believers in their own churches and turn them over to the antichrist forces. This is a time of *apostasy* (Falling away from their faith).

Two witnesses from God begin to stand against the antichrist from the streets of Jerusalem and they continue for 3 ½ years. They will preach the truth of God. Many people will be torn as to whom to believe, the antichrist "answer man" or these two powerful men of God.

The antichrist wants to kill them but so many people world wide are watching them and listening to them, that he can not do it. Finally at the end of the 3 ½ years he does kill them and their dead bodies lie on the streets of Jerusalem for 3 ½ days while most of the world celebrates their death. On the fourth day a loud voice from heaven says, "COME UP HERE", and they are taken up to be with the Lord.

During the first 3 ½ years when the two witnesses were preaching……

A **false prophet** comes on the scene and gives credibility to the antichrist who is now referred to as the beast because he often curses and blasphemes God and even claims to be God. The title "beast" does not refer to his appearance but to his character.

The **false prophet** calls on the people to make an image to the beast and they make one.

The **false prophet** has power to give life to the image of the beast so that it can both speak and cause all those who will **not** worship the beast or take his mark, to be killed.

Note: The image of the beast is an inanimate object, [probably the most powerful and sophisticated computer ever built in the image of a man.]

The antichrist will try to make everyone on earth take an invisible mark, [such as a bar code] in their right hand or forehead and without it they can not buy or sell.

This mark can be used to keep track of people whom the antichrist wants to control or sort out for destruction such as criminals, Jews, or Christians.

Many will take the mark voluntarily but most true Christians will refuse to and they will be labeled enemies of the state (or enemies of humanity) and will be killed for refusing.

Rev. 14: 9-10 says "If any man worship the beast and his image and receives his mark in his forehead, or in his hand, The same shall drink of the wine of the wrath of God, which is poured out without mixture into the cup of His indignation; and he shall be tormented with fire and brimstone in the presence of the holy angels, and in the presence of the Lamb."

Under no circumstances should a believer willingly take the mark of the beast.

Rev. 7: 9-14 John saw a great multitude, which no one could count from every tribe, tongue, people, and nation standing before the throne clothed in white.

One of the elders said, "These are the ones who have come out of great tribulation, and have washed their robes, and made them white in the blood of the Lamb."

We can not necessarily assume that these tribulation martyrs are in heaven because they were raptured. Most likely they died for refusing the mark of the beast.

Although the children of God will undergo tribulation during the first 3 ½ years, they will never undergo the wrath of God. (Rom.5: 9, and 1 Thess. 5: 9) As believers we are at peace with God.

God will get all of His people out of harms way, via the rapture, before the second 3 ½ years of great tribulation begins. He will then pour out His undiluted wrath on the wicked people that are *left behind*. .

Due to the first 3 ½ years of tribulation, the broken treaty by the antichrist and the powerful testimony of the two witnesses, the Jews will be awakened from their spiritual slumber and they will know that Jesus is their true Messiah. They will once again be His people and He will be their God just as He promised.

Part One

~ First ~

3 ½ Years

of Seven

TRIBULATION

REVELATION   Chapter 1   John commissioned to write

Rev.1:1-3 This is **not** the revelation of John, but the revelation of Jesus Christ for John to write about things that must shortly come to pass.

Rev. 1: 9 John was exiled to the island of Patmos due to testifying of the word of God and his testimony of Jesus Christ. John is suffering and feeling the effects of persecution himself.

Rev. 1:10,11 John was in the Spirit on the Lord's Day, (He was worshiping on the Sabbath day), The glorified Jesus appears to the apostle John and tells him to write to the seven churches in Asia Minor (modern day Turkey).

These letters were designed to evaluate their spiritual condition, and to warn and prepare them for the future events that were to come. These 7 churches represent all churches of all ages (seven being the biblical number for completeness).

.**Rev. 1: 17** When John saw the glorified risen Savior he fell, or fainted at His feet. Jesus touched him and kindly said "Fear not, I am the first and the last. Write what you have seen."

Rev. 1:18 Jesus says, "I have the keys of death and hell." Before the crucifixion Satan had the keys of death and hell.

Matt.12:40 says: After the crucifixion, Jesus descended to the heart of the earth for three days. Jesus legally took possession of the keys of death and hell. Because He is sinless, Satan had no authority to keep Him there.

Then He preached the good news of the gospel (the death, burial, and resurrection) to the captives. ***Who are the captives?***

People who died before the resurrection went to Shoal (the place of departed spirits). They either went to the tormented side called Hades or to the comforted side called the bosom of Abraham or Paradise. Luke 16:19-31, Eph.4: 8-10

When Jesus died on the cross He descended into Shoal for 3 days. He legally took the keys of death and hell away from Satan. Then He preached the good news to the captives. The good news was that they could rise with Him on the third day.

After the resurrection, Hades did not change places but the comforted side is now paradise raised (which is called heaven). Now when believers die they are absent from the body, and present with the Lord in heaven. II Corin.5:8

REVELATION   Chapter 2   Letters to Churches

In Rev. *Ch.2-3* The Glorified Jesus dictates to the apostle John on the island of Patmos **letters of evaluation** of the 7 churches of Asia Minor which is modern day western Turkey.

He follows pretty much a standard pattern to each church.

1. Address of the church   Eph., Smy, Perga, Thya, Sardis, Phil., Lao.
2. Attributes of the church   I know your works, suffering, patience, etc.
3. His praise of the church   I know your faithfulness, perseverance, etc.
4. Problems with the church   Left your first love, compromised your faith
5. Prescription for the church   Repent, and remember your first love
6. Promise to the Overcomers   Crown of righteousness; eat of the tree of life.
7. Precaution about hearing   He that has an ear, let him hear, but to those who refuse to repent, I will come quickly and fight against you.

The two churches that receive **no** praise are Sardis & Laodicea. The two churches that have **no** stated problems are Smyrna & Philadelphia. The churches of today could learn much from what was said to each of these 7 churches.

Revelation 2: 1 Unto the angel of the church of **Ephesus** write; these things

(The word angel = ministering spirit) Heb.1:7 kjv

The letter could be to an angel (which isn't very likely because I don't think angels have P.O. Boxes in heaven) **or** more likely John's letter could be to the human minister of the church of Ephesus.

Rev. 2: 2, 3 Jesus says, "I know your works, patience, your distain of evil, your discernment of false teachers." Wow, they're off to a good start.

Rev. 2: 4 Nevertheless, the problem is you have left your first love.

Rev. 2: 5 The prescription is: **Remember** from where you have fallen, **Repent** and **Return** to your first works. (We must not take our faith for granted or become complacent)

Then the promise to the overcomer; Jesus' promise is that they may eat of the tree of life which is in the midst of the paradise of God. That's quite a promise.

Remember access to the tree of life was denied to Adam & Eve after their fall lest they eat and live forever in their fallen state. (Gen.3:22)

Rev. 2: 8, 9 Unto the angel (human minister) of the church of **Smyrna** write;

"I know your works, tribulation, and your poverty, (but you are rich)"

Rev. 2:10 Smyrna was a suffering church. They suffered tribulation, poverty, blasphemy, imprisonment, and death, but their reward was a crown of life.

Verse 10 Some of these faithful saints were imprisoned 10 days, and then killed. One must wonder if 10 days is how long the antichrist will give believers to comply with a state mandate to accept the mark of the beast or be beheaded. Rev.20: 4

Rev. 2:12 To the angel (human minister) of the church in **Pergamos** write...

Rev. 2:13 I know your works, and that you dwell in Satan's territory, (you're not on the safest side of town), but you have **not** denied me, even in the face of martyrdom.

Rev. 2:14 I have a few things against you; you have among you those who hold to the doctrine of Balaam. *Numbers 22-24* Balaam was a Jewish prophet who compromised his faith by receiving payment to seduce Israel into sin. (Such as immorality and eating meat sacrificed to idols)

Rev. 2:16 Repent or I will come quickly and fight against you with the sword of my mouth. (That's called condemnation).

Rev. 2:18 Unto the church in **Thyatira** write; says the Son of God, whose eyes are like a flame of fire and feet like fine brass. *(Rev. 1:14, 15)*

Rev. 2:19 "I know your works, charity, service, and faith, and the last is more than the first." (Their faith out weighed their works).

Rev. 2:20 Nevertheless, you tolerated a "would be" prophetess (Jezebel) who caused Christians to stumble into immorality and defilement.

Rev. 2:21 God gave her time to repent, but she would not.

Rev. 2:22, 23 reads that the Lord will throw her, and her fellow sinners, into a bed of great tribulation, and kill her children. Read **Exodus 34:6-7**

Not necessarily kill her children physically, but when one generation doesn't teach the next about the Lord they are putting them at great risk, spiritually and every other way. And that generation will put the next generation at risk.

REVELATION   Chapter 3   Letters to the Churches

Rev. 3: 1 Unto the angel (human minister) of the church in **Sardis** write; says (Jesus) who has the seven spirits of God.

The 7 spirits of God seem to represent the all knowing, all seeing, omnipresence of God.

"I know your works, your church has a reputation of being alive but you are dead."

When is a church dead? A church is dead when the Holy Spirit has little or no effect on all, or nearly all of the congregation.

Rev. 3: 2 Strengthen what remains before it also dies. Repent, change direction *James 4: 8,* draw nigh unto the Lord, and He will draw nigh unto you.

Isaiah 42:3 A bruised reed he shall not break, a smoking flax he shall not quench. No matter how weak they are in their faith, or how emotionally damaged they are, if they sincerely ask him Jesus will restore them. He'll bind that bruised reed until it's healed, He will fan that smoldering ember until it's a flame of faith. That's just the kindness of the Lord. His prescription for the church of Sardis is:

Rev. 3: 3 remember how you first received Jesus; **hold fast** to that and **repent** before it's too late.

Rev. 3: 4 There are a few in Sardis who have not defiled themselves, they have remained faithful. Isn't that the way it always is? There's always a faithful few in every church and they are the ones who do most of the work.

Rev. 3: 5 Overcomers shall be clothed in white. (White robes represent righteousness)

Rev. 3: 7, 8 Unto the angel (human minister) of the church of **Philadelphia** write: "I know your works, I have set before you an open door.

What is this open door? It is "Freedom in Christ." John 10: 9 Jesus said "I am the door: by me if any man enters in, he shall be saved, and shall go in and out, and find pasture.

Even when this church at Philadelphia was in a weakened state they did not deny Jesus or His word.

Rev. 3:10 kjv, Because you have kept my word of patience, Jesus says "I will keep you from the hour of temptation, which shall come upon all the world"

Jesus did not say I will keep you from *tribulation,* but from *temptation.* Some versions say **trials**. The question is; what are these temptations and trials.

Speaking of the end times Matt.24:24 says many false Christ and false prophets shall show great signs and wonders; insomuch that, if it were possible, they shall deceive even the very elect. (The chosen of God)

Jesus will keep us from the **temptation** to believe that these false prophets and their signs and wonders are for real. He will also keep us from being **tempted** to take the mark of the beast even under severe pressure and persecution.

Jesus does not say in Ch.3:10 that He will keep us from **tribulation.**

Jesus said "In this world you will have tribulation, but be of good cheer, I have overcome the world." *(John 16: 33)*

Christians are not immune to tribulation, but we are immune to the wrath of God because we are at peace with God.

Rev. 3:11, 12 Jesus says in effect "hold on, hang in there, keep your faith and encourage one another."

Rev. 3:14 Unto the angel (human minister) of the church of **Laodicea** write…

Says (Jesus), the faithful and true witness, the beginning of the creation of God.

Contrary to the J. W.'s interpretation of this verse, it's not saying that He is the beginning of the **created** of God. Jesus is **not created**, He is the **creator.**

John 1:1-3 says this: In the beginning was the Word, and the Word was with God, and the Word was God. The same was in the beginning with God. All things were made by Him; and without Him was not anything made that was made.

Colossians 1:14-17 In whom we have redemption through His blood, even the forgiveness of sins: Who is the image of the invisible God, the firstborn of every creature: For by Him were all things created, that are in heaven, and that are in earth, visible and invisible, whether they be thrones, or dominions, or principalities, or powers: all things were created by Him, and for Him:

When verse 14 says Jesus is the beginning of the creation of God it means that "Jesus was the creator from the very beginning of creation."

Rev. 3:15, 16 "I know your works that you are neither cold nor hot, I wish you were one or the other! So because you are lukewarm – neither hot or cold, I will spit you out of my mouth." Luke warm means uncommitted, undecided, or double minded. *Matt 12:30* Jesus said, "He that is not with me is against me."

Rev. 3:17 You say "you are rich and need nothing." They trusted so much in their riches that they were blind to their own wretchedness. Their priorities were not in the right order.

Rev. 3:19 All that God loves He chastens, but He doesn't want to chasten us. Therefore, Jesus says, "Repent."

Rev. 3:20 I stand at the door (of your heart) and knock: **if anyone** hears my voice and opens the door, **I will come in** and eat (commune) with him, and he with me.

We must open the door of our heart; Jesus will not come in uninvited.

From **verse 18 to 22** Jesus does nothing but **woo** the church of **Laodicea** to repent and trust Him to cover their sins.

What an awesome Savior He is. No wonder Jesus said on the cross "Father forgive them for they know not what they do"

REVELATION   Chapter 4   John's Vision of Heaven

Rev. 4: 1 After this, John says "I saw an open door in heaven." After what?

After John wrote the 7 letters to the ministers of the 7 churches in Asia Minor

A voice says **to John** "**Come up here** and I will show **you** things to come"

Many people think that "Come Up Here" is the Pre-tribulation rapture of all believers.

In my opinion it's **not** likely that "Come up here" has anything to do with the rapture. The voice calls **John** up for an expressed purpose, and that is to see and to write about things to come.

Rev. 4: 2 Immediately, "**I**" was in the Spirit (not we), the voice spoke specifically to **John**. So, "Come up here" has nothing to do with the pre-tribulation rapture. If it did the rapture would have happen 2000 years ago, and we would have missed it.

Some say, "The rapture is the next thing on God's calendar of events." *In my opinion that is not true.* There are several more things that must happen before the rapture will occur.

II Thess. 2:1- 4 tells us that before Jesus gathers believers to himself, there shall come a falling away (from the faith), and the man of sin (antichrist) must be revealed, who opposes and exalts himself above all that is called God, and he must sit in the temple of God (not yet built in Jerusalem) showing himself as God.

II Thess. 2:6-8 says: And now we know what withholdeth that he might be revealed in his time. For the ***mystery of iniquity*** doth already work: only he who now letteth will let until he be taken out of the way.

In these verses 6-8 the term "mystery of iniquity" seems to imply that as more and more people refrain from practicing faith in Jesus Christ, the *power* of the Holy Spirit will be more and more withdrawn until the Wicked One can actually be revealed.

Please remember **the *Holy Spirit cannot be completely taken out of the way because He is Omni-present.*** However the *restraining power* of the Holy Spirit will be continuously withdrawn at that time of apostasy. When enough restraining power is withdrawn the antichrist will be revealed, and the rapture will occur sometime after that.

II Thess. 2:6-8 is not likely to be referring to the rapture in these verses because even though there is mention of a continuous removal of the restraining power of the Holy Spirit there is no mention of people being removed.

Also, the persecution of the saints, by the antichrist, must occur before Jesus gathers believers unto Himself. **Rev.13: 7** says: "And it was given unto him (antichrist) to make war with the saints, and to overcome them: and power was given him over all kindred, and tongues, and nations."

The saints will have to be present on earth at the same time the antichrist is for the antichrist to make war with them and to martyr them. *Rev. 13: 7*

Rev. 4: 3 without going into detail, it suffices to say; He that sat upon the throne was magnificent, majestic, and awesome.

Rev. 4: 4 around the throne sat 24 elders clothed in white with gold crowns. Who are the 24 elders? Probably twelve were from the Old Testament, and twelve from the New Testament. (OT, 12 sons of Jacob, which became the twelve tribes of Israel, and the NT, 12 disciples of Jesus; Judas was replaced)

Rev. 4: 6, 8, 9 there were four beasts full of eyes. Who are these four heavenly beings? The word beast can mean heavy load bearer.

Four things I noticed about these 4 heavenly beings: 1. They had 6 wings, 2. They did fly, 3. They cried Holy, Holy, Holy, and 4. They gave glory to God.

Let's go to *Isaiah 6: 2-3* and we will discover exactly who these 4 heavenly beasts are.

Isaiah 6:2-3 above it (The throne of God) stood the Seraphim: each one had **six wings**; with twain he covered his face, and with twain he covered his feet, and with twain he **did fly**. And one cried unto another, and said, **Holy, holy, holy**, earth is full of **his glory**. These 4 beasts are 4 Seraphim angels.

Cherubim angels are innumerable, they seem to be like the worker bees, but Seraphim are seldom mentioned in scripture. They seem to be the more elite angels, very powerful but fewer in numbers, and always close to the throne of God.

Rev. 4: 10, 11 The 24 elders fell down and worshiped saying "Thou art worthy O Lord, for you have created all things and for your pleasure they were created.

All things were created for God's pleasure, including you and me. So, why are we on this earth? *To please God.* It pleased God to put us here and now that we're here we need to please Him. How do we do that? Through worship.

Mark 12: 30, 31 Love the Lord thy God with all your heart, soul, mind, and strength. And love your neighbor as yourself. It finishes up by saying there is no other commandment greater than these. This is pleasing to God.

REVELATION   Chapter 5   The Book with 7 Seals

Rev. 5: 1 The book (scroll) in the right hand of God the Father is a legal document so it is sealed. This book could be the **title deed to the earth**, which Satan legally tricked Adam into turning over to him in the Garden of Eden.

Adam being the only person on earth in the beginning was given ownership of the earth, under the one condition that he **not** partake of the tree of the knowledge of good and evil.

Adam relinquished his ownership by rebelling against God and obeying Satan. Satan became his new master. Adam became Satan's slave and everything Adam owned became Satan's including this world.

II Corin.4:4 Satan is called the god of this world who has blinded the eyes of them who believe not. Satan legally owns this world but God is in control and He will legally take it back through redemption. (Redemption means to redeem or reclaim)

This book (scroll) is written on the inside and outside.

Rev. 5: 2-4 The question is asked, "Who is worthy to open this book and loose the seven seals?" ……. John wept much because no man was found worthy to open this book.

Why was John so upset that no one was worthy in heaven or earth to open this book?

John walked and talked with Jesus, he saw the miracles, and he saw His ascension from the Mt. of Olives into heaven. He must have wondered, *how could Jesus **not** be worthy?*

Rev. 5: 5, 6 An elder said to John "Weep not; the Lion of Judah has prevailed to open the book and to loose the 7 seals."

John saw in the midst of the throne and the 4 beasts and the 24 elders, a Lamb as it had been slain. (Jesus)

Last chapter we determined that the 4 beasts were, **what?** Four Seraphim angels *(Isaiah 6:2-3)* and the 24 elders were, **who?** (12 sons of Jacob of the OT, and 12 disciples of the NT)

Amazingly, John would have actually seen himself as one of those 24 elders in this prophetic vision of the future.

Rev. 5: 7 The Son takes the book from the Father's right hand.

Rev. 5: 9 They sung a new song. Thou art worthy to open the seals for you have redeemed us from every people, tongue, and nation. Who are all these people who have been redeemed from the earth?

Verse 9 In John's heavenly vision he is seeing a multitude of faithful Old Testament believers who are already in heaven **since** the resurrection of Jesus. They were formerly held in "Shoal". (Before the cross, Shoal was the holding place of departed spirits).

This group also includes every New Testament believer who has ever died and gone to heaven up to the time of John's vision. These people were not raptured when John was told to "Come up here". If they were, the rapture would have happened 2000 years ago and we would have missed it. So this first group is any faithful person who has ever died and gone to heaven up to the time of John's heavenly vision.

Rev. 5:11-14 All of heaven burst out into praise and worship of the Lamb who is worthy to open the 7 seals.

MATTHEW — Chapter 24 — The Mt. Olivet Discourse
Matt. 24: 3-26 — Beginning of Sorrows — First 3 ½ years

Matt 24: 1-3 His disciples asked Him "what is the sign of your coming, and of the end of the world?"

Matt. 24: 4, 5 Jesus answer to His disciples is: let no one deceive you for many shall come in my name, saying, I am Christ, and shall deceive many. (Hopefully, not true Christians)

Matt. 24: 6 you shall hear of wars and rumors of wars, be not troubled, the end is not yet.

Matt. 24: 7, 8 There will be famines, and pestilence (often the results of war), but there will also be natural phenomenon such as volcanoes and earthquakes. These are only the beginning of sorrows.

Matt. 24: 9 Then shall they deliver you up (the underground church hiding to avoid having to take the mark of the beast) to be afflicted, and killed, and you shall be hated of all nations for my names' sake. There is a time coming when Christianity will be vilified around the world.

Because Christians will not cooperate or take the mark of the beast, they will be labeled "enemies of the state", or even "enemies of humanity".

Matt. 24:10 Then comes the falling away of the churches in general around the world. Gripped with fear, to protect themselves, they will turn one another over to the authorities. In every church there are strong Christians and weak Christians. The weak and fearful will turn in the strong and faithful.

Matt.10:18-20 says "you shall be brought before governors and kings for my sake, for a testimony against them and the Gentiles. But when they deliver you up, take no thought how or what you shall speak: for it shall be given you in that same hour what you shall speak. It is not you that speak, but the Spirit of your Father that speaks in you.

Matt. 24:11 Many false prophets shall arise (including the antichrist's right hand man), and shall deceive many with **lying words and wonders**. The antichrist and the false prophet are illusionists trying to pass off illusions as legitimate miracles.

Matt. 24:12 Sin, crime, and corruption will be so prevalent at that time that no one will trust anyone. Compassion will be rare. The love of many will grow cold.

Matt. 24:13, 14 this gospel of the kingdom shall be preached in all the world (even during this time of tribulation) for a witness to all nations. Then shall the end come.

We normally think of the modern day Christian church as being commissioned to preach the gospel around the world but this is more likely to be in reference to the two witnesses that God will send. They will preach the gospel around the world at that time.

Rev.11:3 Two witnesses of God will preach the gospel for 3 1/2 years on the streets of Jerusalem as they oppose the antichrist. That will take a lot of hut spa. The whole world will be watching by satellite TV because they are bold enough to stand against the antichrist.

Why can't the antichrist stop them? Because the antichrist has fostered a peace treaty between the Jews and the Arabs for 7 years. No one has ever been able to do this before. This allows the Jews to build their temple and begin sacrificing. The Jews will think of him as their long awaited Messiah.

But after 3 1/2 years when the temple is finished, he breaks the treaty and takes charge of the temple by force to exalt himself as God.   II Thess. 2: 4

Matt. 24:15, 16 (At mid-tribulation) when you see the abomination of desolation spoken of in Daniel, stand in the holy place, then let them which are in Judea flee to the mountains. The Jews will realize that they have been deceived.

Jews who are no longer deceived as to whom their Messiah is and now *saved by the grace of God*, must flee to the mountains without delay or be killed by the forces of the antichrist who are surrounding the city of Jerusalem. *Rev.11: 2*

Matt.24: 17, 18 says: Let him that is on the housetop **not** come down to take anything out of his house. Neither let him which is in the field return back to take his clothes.

It could be that people will be on their housetops watching the temple being built, or in their fields working when they are informed of the takeover of the temple by the antichrist. They will need to immediately take the appropriate action. *They must flee!*

Luke 17: 31-33 says In that day, he which shall be upon the housetop, and his stuff in the house, let him not come down to take it away: and he that is in the field, let him likewise not turn back. Remember Lot's wife. Whosoever shall seek to save his life shall lose it; and whosoever shall lose his life shall preserve it.

Luke 17: 34-37 I tell you, in that night there shall be two men in one bed; the one shall be taken, and the other one left. Two women shall be grinding together; the one shall be taken, and the other left. Two men shall be in the field; the one shall be taken, and the other left.

These verses are **not** referring to the rapture of the saints but rather to the Jewish people in Jerusalem who must flee to the wilderness mentioned in Rev.12: 14 for protection from the forces of the antichrist.

Jewish people who **did** take the mark of the beast will be left alone because they believed the antichrist was their Messiah and willingly received the mark.

Jewish people who **did not** take the mark will be taken at that time regardless of the 7 year treaty that was designed to protect them. When the antichrist breaks that treaty he will try to capture as many of them as he can before they escape to the wilderness.

Luke 17:37 Jesus disciples ask him, "Where Lord" will they be taken? Jesus answers, "Wherever the body is, thither will the eagles (scavengers in this case) be gathered together.

The 144,000 Jews and those who escaped will be protected in the wilderness for the **last** 3.5 years of the great tribulation according to Rev.12:6.

After the 144,000 Jews have accepted Jesus as their Messiah the rapture can occur to take mainly Gentile believers out of harm's way just prior to the wrath of God on the unbelievers who are left behind.

Matt. 24:21 Then shall be great tribulation such as was not since the beginning of the world to this time. God's wrath comes in the second 3 1/2 years of tribulation.

Matt. 24:22 Except those days be shortened, no flesh would be saved, but for the elect's sake, they will be shortened. The elect are the 144,000 Jewish believers who will still be on earth, protected by God, during the last 3 1/2 years of tribulation.

Matt. 24: 23-26 Jesus is warning these protected Jews, "If anyone shall say to you, Lo, here is Christ or there; check out his signs and wonder. **Do not believe them."**

It is a trick designed to draw the Jews out of hiding where they are being fed and protected for the last 3.5 years of the great tribulation. *(Rev. 12:14)*

DANIEL   Chapter 9, 11   Why, Seven Years of Tribulation?

Dan. 9:20-23 (paraphrased) while Daniel was praying, the angel Gabriel touched him and said, "Daniel, you are greatly loved, therefore understand the vision I have given you."

Dan. 9:24 Seventy weeks are determined upon the Jewish people, to finish the transgression, to make an end to their sins, to make reconciliation for iniquity, (make restitution for past sins) and to bring **in** everlasting righteousness. In other words, a dead line of 70 weeks is given for Israel to clean up there act and *to recognize their Messiah.*

One week equals 7 parts of time (A week of days, weeks, months, years, etc.)

The general belief of most commentaries is 70 weeks equals Seventy weeks of years.

Seventy x Seven (years) = 490 years of punishment on the Jewish people, (Most likely for ignoring the Sabbath day of rest and worship).

Lev.26: 34, 35 says this: Then shall the land enjoy her Sabbaths, as long as it lieth desolate, and ye be in your enemies' land; even then shall the land rest, and enjoy her Sabbaths. As long as it lieth desolate it shall rest; because it did not rest in your Sabbaths, when ye dwelt upon it.

Like people, even land needs time to rest and rejuvenate. Otherwise it becomes depleted. So, Israel has 70 weeks of years (490yrs.) to make an end to sin and bring in everlasting righteousness; in other words; to recognize their Messiah. So when does the 490 years begin and when does it end?

Dan. 9:25 tells us that from the time the decree went forth to rebuild Jerusalem unto the Messiah (Jesus) totals 69 weeks of years. So 69 of those 70 weeks have already been accomplished. Then God put the 70th week on hold. He hits the pause button so to speak.

Seventy minus 69 leaves one week or 7 years left over. The pause time between the 69th and 70th week is the church age; the age of grace when God reaches out to the Gentiles because the Jewish people rejected Jesus as their Messiah.

The age of grace is based on **John 3:16.** For God so loved the world, that He gave His only begotten Son, that *whosoever* (Jew or Gentile) believeth on Him should not perish, but have ever lasting life. The age of grace is now about 2000 years down range.

God will restart the clock for the 70th week when the 7 year peace treaty between the Jews and the Arabs is signed.

The church age, in which we are now living, will end with the fullness of the Gentiles. When the last Gentile is saved just before believers are gathered unto the Lord.

Dan. 9:27 He (antichrist) will foster a peace treaty between the Jewish people and the Arabs for one week, (7 years). Immediately the Jews will begin to build their long awaited temple and resume their sacrifices under Old Testament law.

In the **midst** of the seven years, the antichrist will cause all sacrifices to stop (he will break the treaty) and he will take over the temple in Jerusalem by force to exalt himself as God. II Thess.2: 4.

Dan. 11:31 By force of arms shall the antichrist pollute the sanctuary, take away the daily sacrifices, and replace it with the abomination that causes desolation, which most likely is *the image of the beast. (An idol)*

Dan. 11:33 Jewish elders will vehemently object and try to regain control but they will be killed or incarcerated.

Dan. 11:36 Antichrist will do according to his own will, he shall exalt and magnify himself above every god, and shall speak outrageous things against the God of gods.

But what is the purpose of the 7 years of tribulation?

When Jesus came to earth to deliver His people from their sin and oppression, and to set up His kingdom on earth, they did not recognize Him as their Messiah and demanded that He be crucified as an imposter.

He was rejected by the Jews and crucified by the Roman soldiers, dead and buried, but since Jesus is God the Son, He has the power to lay His life down and take it up again. On the third day He arose from the dead and He ascended back to heaven.

Now the Jews are still waiting for their Messiah to come and deliver them from sin and oppression. When actually He has already been here and they have rejected Him.

Because they rejected Him, Romans 11:7-8 says, "God has caused them to have a spirit of slumber", in other words, they are spiritually asleep, while God's Spirit of Grace is spread abroad to the Gentiles.

Israel needs to be awakened so they can see and understand that their true Messiah is Jesus and they can still accept Him even now just as we can by simply believing in Him as our personal Savior. God is still trying to win the Jews back to Himself even though they have rejected Him. **This is the purpose of the 7 years of tribulation.**

II Samuel 7: 24 tells us God will never ever give up on His chosen people, but the Jewish people are steeped in law and tradition and they won't wake up without a major event happening to them.

That major event is called the great tribulation. It is a seven year period of time when terrible things will happen on this earth. *All of these awful events are designed to awaken the Jewish people, and to punish people who have hated God and tried to destroy His people.*

REVELATION   Chapter 6   Six of Seven Seals opened
First 3 ½ years

In John's vision of heaven he sees the Lamb is about to open the book with 7 seals reclaiming what could be **the Title deed to the earth.**

It contains condemnation for the enemies of God, and a battle plan to take back the kingdoms of this world and establish the earthly kingdom of Christ. **Rev.11:15**

Rev. 6: 1, 2 In John's vision of heaven he sees the Lamb (Jesus) open the **first seal.**

He sees a **white horse** and the rider has a bow and a crown. He goes out to conquer.

A white horse means he appears to be a valiant leader, a bow means he does not appear to be very threatening, a crown means he speaks with authority. His goal is to conquer people. Not necessarily to kill them but to control them. Many say this rider is the antichrist but I don't think so; I think the rider on the pale horse in verse 8 is more likely to be the antichrist.

This rider on the white horse could be a powerful world statesman who will rapidly organize, pressure, and force countries to unite into 10 kingdom empires later to be ruled by the antichrist. This white horse rider is a worldwide community organizer. Each of the 10 kingdoms will be composed of several counties. Antichrist will appoint their 10 kings.

Because the rider in Verse 2 is on a white horse does **not** necessarily make him a good guy, especially since he is followed by three more hellish horsemen.

Rev. 6: 3, 4 Second seal, Red horse, the rider was given power to take peace from the earth. If he takes peace from the earth! What's left? There will be constant wars and rumors of wars. These are not big wars, or nuclear wars, but worldwide skirmishes.

People tend to fear rapid change. They will be concerned about what will happen if their countries are clustered into kingdoms and how that might affect their borders, laws, freedoms, and their national sovereignty. Some countries will violently resist these sudden changes.

Rev. 6: 5 Third seal, Black horse whose rider had a pair of balances in his hand which could imply that this will be a time of shortages, or contrived shortages, or rationing of necessities. (A time of desperation) Shortages and rationing are often the result of wars.

It's likely that the antichrist will emerge as a problem solver and assure the world that not much will change as a result of their being included into one of the kingdoms of the world and there might even be mutually shared benefits. This will make sense to most people and they will settle down and come on board. *The antichrist will have rapidly achieved his goal of establishing the 10 world kingdoms.*

Rev. 6: 7, 8 Fourth Seal, that Jesus opens reveals a **Pale horse.** The name of the rider was Death; and Hell followed him.

The rider named *"Death"* could be the **antichrist**, and the one named, *"Hell"* could be the **false prophet** spoken of in Rev.13:11, 12.

Power was given to Death and Hell (By Satan of course) to kill ¼ of the earth's population in three ways.

1. **By sword** - martyrs beheaded for refusing the mark of the beast. Rev.20:4

2. **Hunger** - because they can not buy or sell without the mark. Rev.13: 17

3. **Beasts of the field** - we can only speculate as to how this might happen but most of these people are killed, or allowed to die, for not taking the mark of the beast.

Rev. 6: 9 Fifth Seal is opened; John saw **under the altar, the souls** of them who were slain for the word of God and for their testimony. These are faithful martyrs and overcomers, but why are they under the altar?

Their bodies are in graves but their souls are in **close proximity** to God. Under the altar could imply that they are pleading for justice at the feet of God. (Rev 8:3)

Note: That the location of the golden altar is before the throne of God. It contains the prayers of all who have been wronged, but have trusted God to take vengeance on their enemies.

Rev 6:10 They cried with a loud voice, *"How long Oh Lord, holy and true, dost thou not judge and avenge our blood on them that dwell on the earth?"*

Verse 10 Implies that, as of the fifth seal, the Lord has not yet begun to take revenge on the wicked people of the earth.

6: 11 First things first, even before answering their question, they were given white robes (which represent righteousness) and then invited to enter into a heavenly rest.

First He wants them to know how proud He is of them, so He gives them white robes of righteousness. He asked them to relax and to trust Him to deal with their enemies. Then He explained to them that more of their fellow servants must be killed as they were.

This strongly implies that as of the fifth seal the rapture has not yet taken place, nor has the wrath of God. The antichrist is still making war with the saints for refusing to take the mark of the beast. Rev.13:7 (So, the saints have to be present on earth during the first 3 ½ years of tribulation)

Rev. 6:12-14 When the **Sixth Seal** is opened there will be a powerful **worldwide earthquake** that moves every mountain and island out of its place. The sun, moon, and stars are darkened, perhaps due to volcanic ash. An earthquake of this magnitude would trigger worldwide volcanic action.

This earthquake, as horrible as it is, is a natural disaster. It is **not** the wrath of God. The actual wrath of God can **not** begin until all believers are out of harms way. Although believers are subject to tribulation they are not subject to the wrath of God. Rom.5:9, Rom.8:1, I Thess.5:9

As of the sixth seal the rapture has **not** taken place, nor has the wrath of God. There are only 7 seals. So, the 7th seal will be the wrath of God in the second 3 ½ years of the great tribulation.

The chart on the following page shows that our study has completed **Part One**.

Order of Events

Part One	**Book of Revelation Order of Events** **First 3 1/2 of 7 years Tribulation** Ch. 1-3 letters to 7 churches Ch. 4, 5 John's vision of heaven Ch. 6 **Six of Seven Seals Opened** 1st white horse 2nd red horse 3rd black horse 4th pale horse 5th martyrs under altar 6th great earthquake
Part Two	**First 3 1/2 Long Interlude** between 6th and 7th seal **Ch.7 and Ch.10-14** Ch.7 144,000 sealed Ch.10 the edible book Ch.11 the two witnesses Ch.12 woman (Israel) protected Ch.13. antichrist & false prophet Ch.14 the rapture chapter

Order of Events

Part Three	**Second 3 1/2 of 7 years Tribulation** **The Wrath of God** Ch. 8, 9, and Ch. 15-18 **Seventh Seal—Contains 7 Trumpets and 7 Bowls** **Seventh Trumpet—Contains 7 Bowls**
Part Four	Ch. 19-22 **Marriage of the Lamb** **Armageddon** **Millenial Reign of Christ** **White Throne Judgment** **New Heaven & New earth** **New Jerusalem**

REVELATION Chapter 7 The 144,000 Sealed
First 3 ½ year *The Interlude*

This long interlude between the 6th and 7th seal includes chapters 7 and 10-14. These chapters seem to inform us of things that happen intermittently, during the first 3 ½ years, as the first six seals are opened.

Rev 7: 1 Four angels are standing on the four corners of the earth holding back the winds.

What winds? The windstorms of God's judgment

We know the earth is round, but the **four corners** of the earth could refer to the four corners of a compass North, South, East, and West, the totality of the earth.

Rev. 7: 2, 3 A fifth angel tells the first four angels **not** to hurt the earth or sea until the servants of God are sealed in their foreheads.

Rev.7:4-8 The total number of those who were sealed is 144,000. There were twelve thousand from each of the 12 tribes of Israel. They may or may not know why they have been marked in their foreheads. It's only important that God knows why.

Sealed means secured or preserved, **not** necessarily saved at this time. (We **can't** make that assumption yet). The salvation of the 144,000 will be confirmed at a later point in time.

This seal on the 144,000 means that they have been set apart and protected from any harm that could be coming their way.

The 144,000 are "true Jews" having no Gentile blood mixed into them through intermarriage. They legally represent and identify the true nation of Israel. When they accept Jesus they will qualify to be the **first fruits** unto God and the Lamb.

Rev. 7: 9, 10 After this, John suddenly sees a multitude, which no man could number, standing before the throne from every nation, kindred, people, and tongue clothed in white. Who are they?

Rev. 7: 11, 12 They cried loudly, "Salvation to our God and to the Lamb", and the entire heavenly host began to worship.

Rev. 7: 13 One of the elders asks John "What are all these people doing here, and where did they come from?"

Rev. 7: 14-17 John says "Sir, you know", (This is not a question but a statement) and the elder said, "These are they which **came out of great tribulation** and have washed their robes and made them white in the blood of the Lamb. They will never hunger, or thirst again, and God will wipe away all their tears."

Note: If these believers have come out of great tribulation, (Guess what?) **they must have been in it** during the opening of the first six seals in Ch.6.

We can **not** assume that these tribulation martyrs are in heaven because they were raptured. Most likely they were martyred for refusing the mark of the beast.

They will be martyred in large numbers (millions worldwide) during the first 3 ½ years of tribulation while antichrist is actively pursuing his one world agenda.

If this huge group of believers were raptured before the tribulation began, then they could **not** have come out of great tribulation as the elder said they did.

Some might wonder if this huge group of believers who were martyred might have been saved after the pre-tribulation rapture took place. My question to them would be: Who will lead them to the Lord if all Gentile believers are gone?

How will the faith of these baby Christians be so well developed in that short 3 ½ year period of time, and in such an hostile environment, that they will become the source of all the millions of martyrs mentioned in Revelation. It's just not likely to happen that way.

Was it too late for people to come into Noah's ark once God had closed the door? (Yes)

After all these centuries, isn't it more likely that God would be willing to postpone the rapture 3 ½ more years to include all of these new believers that will be saved as a result of hearing the two witnesses preach during the first 3 ½ years of the tribulation? Rev. 11: 3

This completes chapter 7. Chapter 8 begins the second 3 ½ years with the opening of the seventh and last seal.

However, since our study is designed to divide the seven years of tribulation into two parts so that we can study each half by itself, we will put chapters 8 and 9 on hold, because they are part of the second half.

We will jump to Ch.10 because it is part of the first 3 ½ years of tribulations.

REVELATION   Chapter 10   The Edible Book
First 3 ½ years   *Interlude between 6th and 7th Seal*

Rev. 10: 1 John sees a mighty angel descend from heaven. His appearance was very bright and he was arrayed in splendor. (This is a glorious and powerful angel.)

Rev. 10: 2 He held in his hand a little book (opened). His right foot was set on the sea and his left foot on land.

One foot on the sea and the other on land implies that this mighty angel is staking a claim to the earth, since the entire surface of the world is basically comprised of water and land.

Rev. 10: 3 says: He roared like a lion standing over its' prey, daring anyone to challenge his claim.

Rev.10: 8 the voice from heaven tells John to "Go take the little book, which is open, out of the hand of the mighty angel that stands on the sea and the earth."

Rev.10: 9, 10 When John asks for the book, the angel tells him to "take it and eat it up; and it will make your belly bitter, but it will be sweet as honey in your mouth."

John took the book and ate it up. It was sweet in his mouth but made his belly bitter. The question is: What is this little book and what information does it contain? The best way to answer this is to use related scripture.

Ezekiel 2: 8-10 says this, "Son of man, hear what I say unto thee; be not thou rebellious like that rebellious house: (of Israel) open thy mouth, and eat that I give thee. And when I looked, behold, a hand was sent unto me; and lo, a roll of a book was therein; and he spread it before me (He opened it); and it was written within and without: and there was written therein lamentations, and mourning, and woe."

The little book, most likely is the "Word of God". Though it contains the sweetness of the true prophecies of God, it also contains lamentations, judgments, and woe about the wrath of God upon the wicked kingdoms of this world.

Rev.10:11 John is told that he must prophecy to many people, nations, tongues, and kings. The question is: How can John be expected to do this; he is elderly and he is exiled to the small island of Patmos in the Aegean Sea?

Bibles will still be available in the end times. The remainder of John's writings will contain prophecies to people, nations, tongues, and kings. His writings are now seen in five books of our present bible. John wrote the gospel of John, I, II, III John, and Revelation.

REVELATION   Chapter 11 A   Two Witnesses
First 3 ½ years   *Interlude between 6th and 7th Seal*

Rev. 11: 1 John is told to measure the temple of God, the altar, and those who worship there. The question is: How do you measure people who worship?

Usually, when measurements are taken in the bible, it is to evaluate the spiritual condition of the people of God. For example: The plumb line in the book of *Amos Ch.* 7: 8 represented the accuracy of God's word; the standard of truth by which Israel could **gauge** themselves spiritually. Another example is Rom.3:23 All have sinned and come ***short*** of the glory of God.

This temple is **not** yet built in Jerusalem but John is seeing it in the future.

Rev. 11: 2 John is told **not** to measure outside of the temple, because it is given to the Gentiles, and they shall tread the holy city under foot for 3 ½ years.

The question is: What is keeping these Gentiles in and around the Holy City (Jerusalem) for 3 ½ years? Why are they there?

After the antichrist fosters a 7 year peace treaty between the Jews and the Arabs, the armed forces of the antichrist are surrounding the city to protect the Jews from belligerent Arabs while the Jews build their temple in Jerusalem; a temple that the antichrist secretly intends to hijack for his own use as soon as it is finished.

Although some Arabs might know the antichrist's secret plan; Israel will be completely unaware of this because they will think the antichrist is the Messiah they have been waiting for ever since they rejected Jesus.

Rev. 11: verses 3, 4 speak of two consecrated witnesses sent by God who are clothed in sackcloth implying that they, like John the Baptist, have no interest in material gain. Their motives are pure as they oppose the antichrist and preach the gospel around the world by Satellite television. **Matt.24:14**

When these two witnesses preach the gospel, the whole world will listen because of their boldness in opposing the antichrist.

It's true that the Christian community should preach the gospel around the world, and we do make a valiant effort, but how much of the world is actually listening and responding? This is not saying anything against the awesome work that missionaries do, but they will never have a bully pulpit to oppose the antichrist like these two witnesses will have. Nor will they have a pulpit of power to preach the gospel around the world with all the media coverage that will be given to these two witnesses.

Some speculate that these two witnesses will be Elijah and Enoch, the only two people recorded in the bible who have never died. Both were simply "caught up" to heaven, although, "it's appointed to everyone once to die." Heb. 9:27

Rev. 11: 5, 6 Some speculate the two anointed ones will be Elijah and Moses because of the similar types of miracles that they did.

They will stand up for God and against the antichrist for 3 ½ years. It's an ironic situation because of the seven year treaty. While the temple is being built, the Jews are being protected by the same people who will later try to destroy them.

Most of the people around the world will be constantly watching by satellite TV. They will be torn as to where to place their loyalty. Should they side with these two powerful men of God who do miracles and preach their hearts out to a world where the love of many has grown cold, **or**

Should they side with this charismatic world statesman who seems to have a lot of new ideas for how to solve the world's problems? However, he tends to speak outrageous things against God.

The two witnesses will stand up for God and against the antichrist for 3 ½ years. While their temple is being built in the background. The antichrist wants to kill these two witnesses, to shut them up, but he can't do it yet, for three reasons, they are too popular, too powerful, and he has made a peace treaty with Israel for 7 years.

Rev 11: 7 When they finish their testimony, after 3 ½ years, the antichrist will make war with them and kill them, as his forces hijack the newly finished temple.

Rev.11: 8, 9, 10 It seems to the world the antichrist has prevailed over these two men of God who have been tormenting and convicting the conscience of the world for so long.

Although multitudes have been saved by their powerful testimony, most of the world is happy about their deaths and will **not** even allow their bodies to be buried. In fact they celebrate as their dead bodies lie in the streets of Jerusalem for 3 ½ days the world rejoices and gloats.

While their dead bodies lie in the streets in Jerusalem, the antichrist's forces will hijack the temple, stop the Jewish sacrifices, and set up the abominable image of the beast; which is a man made idol that the world will be commanded to worship. *Dan.11:31*

The image of the beast could be quickly relocated to the newly built temple from another location, perhaps a country from within the former Roman Empire because that's where the antichrist's headquarter city is likely to be located.

REVELATION   **Chapter 11 B**   **Two Witnesses**
First 3 ½ years   *Interlude between 6th and 7th Seal*

Rev. 11:11 After 3 ½ days the spirit of life from God enters into them and they stand up.

Great fear falls on all those who see them. (These men had power over all plagues).

Rev. 11:12 *They* heard a great voice from heaven say unto **them** "COME UP HERE" and *they* ascended to heaven in a cloud as *their* enemies watched.

Some believe that this is when that great voice is calling **all** believers to "COME UP HERE", but if that were the case, then the rapture could be pinpointed to an exact moment in time. Three and one half days from the time of their murders.

That would be scripturally problematic because Jesus said, "no one but my Father knows the day or the hour when the trumpet shall sound and the Son of man will come to meet believers in the air." Matt.24:30, 31and Matt.24:36

So, *"COME UP HERE"* is not in reference to the rapture of all believers. The great voice is only calling the two witnesses to come up.

Rev. 11:13 Immediately after the "catching away" of the two witnesses, there is a great earthquake in Jerusalem that destroys 1/10 of the city and kills 7000 people. Many of the 7000 will be Gentiles who were there treading down the city for 3 ½ years. *Rev.11:2*

The Gentiles were surrounding Jerusalem to enforce a 7 year peace treaty. They are there to protect Israel from belligerent Arabs while the Jews build their temple.

It's likely that this earthquake will hit the edge of town and take out one section of that circumference. This earthquake could provide the Jews an escape route from this killing field they are in, if they move quickly.

Matt.24:15-21 says: When ye therefore shall see the abomination of desolation, spoken of by Daniel the prophet, stand in the holy place, (whoso readeth, let him understand :) Then let them which be in Judea flee into the mountains: Let him which is on the housetop not come down to take anything out of his house: Neither let him which is in the field return back to take his clothes. And woe unto them that are with child, and to them that give suck in those days. But pray ye that your flight be not in the winter, neither on the Sabbath day: For then shall be great tribulation, such as was not since the beginning of the world to this time, no, nor ever shall be.

The powerful testimonies of the two witnesses, followed by this devastating earthquake, frightens the **remnant** so much that they begin to glorify the God of heaven. *(Rom.9:27)*

Rev.11:13 is the first record of the 144,000 giving glory to the God of heaven. Up to this point they were steeped in the O.T. law, and willing to accept the antichrist as their Messiah.

The remnant is the 144,000 true Jews who were sealed, but not necessarily saved in *Ch.7*.

At that time they were sealed from harm, but not unto salvation. ***But now.... Praise God, here in Ch.11, this is the point at which the elect of Israel are finally saved after all these centuries.***

They are finally rejecting the antichrist as their Messiah because he has set up a despicable idol in their temple, and accepting Jesus Christ because of the earthquake and the powerful testimony of the two witnesses.

The 144,000 are "true Jews" having no Gentile blood mixed into them, and therefore **as believers**, they now qualify to be the **first fruits** unto God and the Lamb.

Rom.1:16 says the **gospel of Christ** is the power of God, unto salvation, to everyone that believes, **to the Jew first,** (first fruits) and also to the Greek. (Gentiles)

The 144,000 are the first fruit unto God, but the worldwide church (body of believers) is the main harvest. (It is comprised mostly of Gentiles).

Now that the 144,000 true Jews are saved and will **not** lose their salvation, the rest is academic. Satan can no longer save himself from the lake of fire by deceiving the Jews as to whom their Messiah is. Now Satan's only hope of **foiling** God's most important prophecy: *Ezekiel 37: 27, 28* is to destroy them.

Ezekiel 37: 27, 28 says this: My tabernacle also shall be with them: yea, I will be their God, and they shall be my people. And the heathen shall know that I the Lord do sanctify Israel, when my sanctuary shall be in the midst of them for evermore.

In this future scenario **the 144,000 true Jews recognize Jesus as their Messiah.** Israel recognizing Jesus as their Messiah is the main reason for the 7 years of tribulation.

John 1:10, 11 *When Jesus came the first time,* He came to His own, and His own people recognized Him **not** (as their Messiah), but now they do. Now it's a whole new ball game between God and Satan.

When Satan can no longer deceive the Jews, then his only other option will be to destroy them so that Jesus can not reign over them on this earth when He returns. (This is in reference to the millennial reign of Christ)

REVELATION   **Chapter 12 A**   The Woman (Israel)
First 3 ½ years   *Interlude between 6th and 7th Seal*

Rev. 12: 1 There appeared a great wonder in heaven. A ***woman*** clothed with the sun and the moon under her feet and on her head a crown of 12 stars. Who is this woman? The way to uncover this symbolism is to use related scripture.

Gen. 37: 9, 10 (paraphrased). He (Joseph) dreamed another dream, and told it to his brothers, and said "The Sun, and the moon, and the eleven stars ***bowed down*** to me." And he told it to his father and his father **rebuked** him and said "Shall I and thy mother and thy brethren indeed bow down unto thee?

The question is: In Joseph's dream, whom do the sun, moon, and 11 stars represent? They represent Joseph's father, mother, and 11 brothers, the sons of Jacob. So, Jacob himself interprets who the sun, moon, and stars are. But who is the woman?

What Nation emerged from this family? **(Israel)** Gen.35:10-12 tells us that God changed Jacob's name to Israel.

Can we conclude that **the woman** in verse 1 with the sun, moon, and 12 stars might **symbolize the nation of Israel?**

Rev. 12: 2, 5 She being with child cried, travailing in birth, and pain to be delivered. She gave birth to a ***son*** who was to rule all nations with a rod of iron. Here again we need to use related scripture.

Psalms 2: 7-9 (paraphrased) the Lord has promised; you are my Son. I will give you the nations, and you will rule them with an iron rod.

Since Jesus is God the Father's only begotten Son can we conclude that **the son** born of the woman (Israel) in verse 2 **symbolizes Jesus?**

Rev.12: 3 In this verse appears another wonder in heaven; a great red dragon having 7 heads, 10 horns, and 7 crowns.

Rev.12: 9 says, the great dragon was cast out, that old serpent called the Devil and Satan.

Can we conclude that the **great red dragon** in verse 3 is **symbolic of Satan**?

Rev.12: 3 says "The dragon has 7 heads, 10 horns, and 7 crowns." Let's put this on hold to avoid teaching it repetitiously because we will get into this same symbolism when we get to *Chapter 13 and 17.*

Rev.12: 4 In John's vision of the future he sees the Dragon's tail drew 1/3 of the stars of heaven and cast them to the earth. **Rev.1: 20** we learned that stars can mean angels.

The dragon's tail **drew** 1/3 of the angels of heaven and cast them to the earth, but please don't think of his tail like a broom that swept 1/3 of the angels out of heaven.

The original meaning of the word **drew** is not to sweep like a broom, but to hale, call, or draft and when Satan "haled them" his angels followed him to the earth. But why did they follow him?

A major event is about to happen on earth, and Satan wants all his forces on hand to help him destroy this man-child that's about to be delivered by the woman (the nation Israel.)

So, this might be in reference to the birth of Jesus.

Rev. 12: 5 She delivers a son who will rule all nations with a rod of iron (Rev.19:15), but her son was caught up unto the throne of God.

Satan failed to destroy Jesus at birth when King Herod ordered all baby boys in the area of Bethlehem less than 2 years of age to be killed, *however* Jesus did give up His life on the cross and then He was resurrected (caught up) to the right hand throne of God.

Rev. 12: 7- 9 War breaks out in heaven between the dragon and one third of the angels and Michael plus the remaining two thirds of the angels, and Michael (The archangel) wins.

Satan will be demoted, and apparently Michael will be promoted to his place as the chief ranking angel. From that time on Satan (the accuser of the brethren) will have no more access to heaven.

Until that point in time Satan will continue to have full access to come and go between earth and heaven and to make accusations against believers before the throne of God. That's what Satan does now; night and day.

Satan is allowed to keep his place in heaven even after his fall, just as man kept earth after his fall. But at this time **in the future**, he and his angels will be permanently band from heaven. (Cast down to the earth, never to return to heaven).

REVELATION Chapter 12 B The Woman (Israel)
First 3 ½ years *Interlude between 6th and 7th Seal*

Rev. 12: 12 Therefore, you who dwell in heaven, rejoice! Because Satan (the accuser), and his angels are permanently gone.

The Devil is come down to earth with great wrath because he knows his time is short.

His time is short to do what? (To destroy God's people, the Jews, before he's bound, and cast into the bottomless pit for 1000 years). **Rev. 20:1-3** Satan knows scripture, so he knows this is going to happen to him. His time is short to destroy the Jewish people.

All prophecy in scripture pertains to the Jewish people. If Satan can foil God's prophecies and promises to the Jewish people then God would become a liar like Satan is.

If that could be true God would **not** be able to legally condemn Satan to the lake of fire where he will be tormented day and night forever and ever. (Rev.20:10) The lake of fire is Satan's greatest fear!

Rev.12:13, 14 tell us the dragon is very angry about being cast out of heaven to earth and begins to persecute the woman (Israel). But the woman is given two wings of a great eagle to fly into the wilderness where she is nourished and protected for the last 3 ½ years of tribulation.

Eagle's wings in scripture are usually symbolic of ***divine deliverance.*** Two eagle wings are given to the woman (Israel). *Isaiah 40:31 also Exodus 19:4*

Exodus 19: 4 says ye have seen what I did unto the Egyptians, and how I bare you on eagles' wings, and brought you unto myself.

Notice that in verses 13, and 14 the woman (Israel) is protected for the last 3 ½ years of the tribulation, implying that Israel is still here on earth for the entire 7 years of the tribulation. *(Rev.12: 6)*

REVELATION   Chapter 13 A   Antichrist (beast) Revealed
First 3 ½ years   *Interlude between 6th and 7th Seal*

Rev. 13: 1 In John's vision he sees a beast rise up out of the sea having **seven heads, ten horns, and ten crowns**. This is not likely to be a sea of water that would produce such a beast.

Rev. 17:15 tells John "**the waters** you saw **are people, multitudes, nations, and languages**". Therefore, it's more likely that the beast came up out of the sea of humanity.

The beast is human, but symbolically he has 7 heads, 10 horns, and 10 crowns. The word "beast" does not refer to his appearance but to his character. He is a monster in disguise.

Dan.7: 24 informs us that the 10 horns are 10 kings. They represent a coalition of 10 end-time kingdoms. Each kingdom will be composed of many countries. They are 10 kings with 10 crowns that are led by and coordinated by the antichrist.

Rev.17: 9 states that **the 7 heads are 7 hills** on which the woman sits. The woman in Ch.12 was symbolic of Israel, but this woman is symbolic of evil.

We will learn later in Ch.17 that **this woman is symbolic of an evil world system.** She is Mystery Babylon, the great harlot; the headquarter city of the antichrist.

Mystery Babylon will probably be located somewhere in the former Roman Empire and will be supported by these 10 world kingdoms. Each kingdom will be composed of many countries.

Dan.7: 24 informs us that; this coalition will begin with 10 distinct world kingdoms, but will be reduced to 7 when the "little horn" (antichrist) uproots three of them, and then incorporates their resources into the remaining coalition of seven.

Most likely the three kings that were uprooted were **not** in full compliance with the antichrist's "one world" agenda. Rev.17:12-14 implies that the three uprooted kings will be replaced before the attack on Israel begins at Armageddon, therefore I may refer to them in the future as 10 world kingdoms.

Characteristics of the antichrist:

Dan.7: 8 He begins as a little horn (king) who has a mouth speaking great things. (As in, outrageous things) He will be a dynamic, charismatic orator.

Dan.7: 25 He will speak great words against the most high and shall wear out the saints.

It's much easier for him to make accusations against God, than it is for believers to defend against them.

He will threaten to change times and laws. This may also be wearisome to the saints because these will probably be "tried and true" traditions that need nothing changed.

Dan.11:36 states that this reprobate will do according to his own will; he will arrogantly exalt and magnify himself above every god and speak against the God of gods.

Dan.11: 37 tells us he will **not** regard the "**God of his fathers.**" This could imply that he is Jewish. Jews are well known for keeping records of the God of their fathers. It's not likely that Israel would ever consider anyone other than a Jew to be their Messiah.

Nor will he regard the desires of women. This could imply that he is homosexual or simply has very little respect for women. Nor does he regard any god at all.

Dan.9: 27 He will foster a peace treaty between the Arabs and Israel for one week of years (7 years), allowing them time to build their temple. Then after 3 ½ years when the temple is finished, he will break the treaty and take over the temple by force, to exalt himself as God. He is a liar and a truce breaker.

II Thess. 2: 4 speaking of the antichrist says: Who opposeth and exalteth himself above all that is called God, or that is worshiped; so that he as God sitteth in the temple of God, showing himself that he is God. He is an impostor. The term "anti" means against, but it also means "instead of."

Rev.11:7 He is the beast from the bottomless pit. (From the pit of Hell)

Rev.13: 3 One of the antichrist's heads will be mortally wounded but the wound will be healed. The world will think he is supernatural. It could be a failed assassination attempt by an overly zealous so called Christian, giving the antichrist a valid excuse to make war with the saints.

Possibly the head wound (assassination attempt) may have been to one of the antichrist's "doubles" (if he has them). Verse 3 says **"one of his heads"** was wounded to death implying that he may use "look alike doubles."

Sadam Husain, former leader of Iraq, used several different look alike doubles for public appearances due to assassination threats and attempts.

It's not likely that the antichrist was actually killed and came back to life. It was an illusion. He does not have the power to lay down his life and take it up again. Only Jesus can do that because He is "the resurrection and the life." *John 11:25*

Rev. 13: 4 The world begins to **worship** the dragon (Satan) that gave power to the beast, saying "Who is like the beast, and who is able to make war with him."

This tells us that the antichrist is a powerful global military leader, and has access to weapons of mass destruction. He is very intimidating.

Rev.13: 5, 6 Satan gave the antichrist a mouth to speak blasphemies against God for 3 ½ years. *(Dan.7:25)* How long was Jesus' earthly ministry? (3 1/2 years)

Rev.13: 7 Satan gives the antichrist power to make war with the saints and to overcome them. While the antichrist is verbally attacking God and all who dwell in heaven, he is physically attacking the saints on earth.

For the antichrist to make war with the saints, they have to be present on this earth at the same time he is, even as late as chapter 13. The rapture is not yet, but it's getting closer.

Rev.13: 7 Satan also gave the antichrist power over all kindred, tongues, and nations. The entire world will be in his grip. His goal is to be the king of all the kings and kingdoms of the earth. (He would be a counterfeit king of kings and lord of lords).

Rev. 13: 8 Most people who dwell on earth, whose names are **not** written in the Lamb's book of life, will worship the antichrist. He meets very little resistance as he rises to power.

Those who do oppose the antichrist are overcome and martyred by the thousands. *Verse 7*

REVELATION
First 3 ½ years

Chapter 13 B — Antichrist (beast) and The False Prophet

Rev.13: 11 John sees another beast come up out of the earth. The first beast came up from the sea. Why does this beast come up from the earth? No one seems to know for sure.

He had two horns like a lamb implying that he is less threatening than the first beast which had 10 horns. This beast has only two, like a lamb, and yet he speaks as a dragon.

Rev. 13: 12 He is actually just as dangerous as the antichrist, because he exercises all the power of the first beast and causes all the earth to worship the beast. How? He gives creditability to the antichrist. The first beast (antichrist) is a political leader; the second beast (The false prophet) is a religious leader. That's why he's called a prophet.

The antichrist might have Jewish ancestors because it's not likely that Israel would ever consider anyone other than a Jew to be their Messiah. If the antichrist is Jewish then it's likely that the false prophet might be also.

Moses **had** Aaron (a priest) to speak for him, Jesus **had** John the Baptist (a preacher) to prepare the way for him; and the antichrist will have a spokesman (a prophet) to prepare the way for him and to exalt and magnify his **false** glory.

Rev. 13:13 The false prophet performs signs and wonders such as calling fire down from heaven, but don't forget what is said in…

II Thess.2: 9 Even him, whose coming is after the working of Satan with all power and signs and lying wonders.

By the power of Satan, the antichrist will perform signs and lying wonders. He and the false prophet are illusionists. They are masters of deception.

II Thess. 2: 11, 12 informs us that, for this cause God shall send people strong delusions, that they should believe a lie: that they all might be damned who believed not the truth, but had pleasure in unrighteousness.

Rev. 13: 14 Now that most people of the earth are deceived, and awestruck by the so called "miracles" the false prophet declares that they should **make an image to the beast.**

He reminds them of the mortal head wound received by the beast, that was supernaturally healed. He seemed to have risen from the dead, a counterfeit to Christ's resurrection.

The antichrist hates Christians because it was probably an overly zealous "so called Christian" who tried to kill him with a sword to the head. It's a great excuse for him to vilify Christians, to target them, and make war with them. *(Rev.13: 7)*

Christians are his chief opposition until he finally just wears them out with relentless accusations against them and the Most High God.

Rev. 13:15 The false prophet had power to give life to the "image of the beast." ***Stop!***

As Christians we know that the false prophet can not give life to anything, and certainly not to this inanimate, man made object. Only God can give life.

However, he could make it **appear** to have life. This is another one of his illusions.

The false prophet makes the image of the beast speak. This implies that the image is in the form and likeness of the antichrist. (It is a very sophisticated computerized robot).

No human being other than Jesus Christ could ever be smart enough to successfully be the king of the entire world so antichrist will utilize this powerful computer to assist him.

The latest state of the art technology will be used to make it so realistic that no one will be able to tell if it is the real antichrist or his robotic image.

It will be equipped with a powerful computer that can make all of his sounds and movements seem very realistic. Most of its technology will be behind walls or curtains.

With previously gathered data, this preprogrammed robotic "talking head" will have the ability to decide who lives or dies based on their loyalty to the beast and his one world agenda.

Jesus said "He that is not with me is against me" *(Matt.12:30)* Antichrist will basically be saying the same thing by demanding that everyone take the mark of the beast; thereby identifying themselves with him by receiving the mark, **or** identifying themselves against him by refusing the mark.

Rev. 13:16, 17 The ten king coalition led by the antichrist causes all levels of society worldwide to take a mark in their right hand or in their forehead. Without this mark they can not buy or sell. That's a big problem. How will they obtain the necessities for life? How will they support their families?

The mark is likely to be an invisible type of bar code. Some type of a laser mark applied quickly and painlessly, or possibly a computer chip applied hypodermically under the skin.

Many will take the mark voluntarily because it will be presented as a great idea for solving some of the world's most pressing problems, such as **catching criminals.**

The first time they try to buy anything, the police will be there to arrest them.

Other uses might be to **find missing persons** such as children. Scanners will be installed in public places to help find kidnapped or run away children.

Authenticating people's identity, this worldwide system would be owned and operated by antichrist loyalists from one central location. Most likely, it will be a country within the former Roman Empire.

Outside intervention into this secured system would be very difficult without giving up your own identification and location.

Buying and selling over the internet might require a web cam or a web scan to complete the transaction. Lost or stolen credit cards would be a thing of the past.

Many will take the mark simply **out of fear** of not being able to buy or sell necessities such as groceries, medicine, utilities, fuel, and parts for vehicles.

Unfortunately, some will accept it because their home church advised them to do so.

Some will refuse the mark of the beast for religious reasons, because their home church advised them to, or they might make a personal choice based on Rev.14: 9, 10

Rev.14: 9, 10 If any man worship the beast and his image, and receive his mark in his forehead or in his hand, the same shall drink of the wine of the wrath of God, which is poured out without mixture into the cup of his indignation; and he shall be tormented with fire and brimstone in the presence of the holy angels, and in the presence of the Lamb.

These are powerful words; **under no circumstances should any believer willingly receive the mark of the beast.**

The system will require that everyone come on board. It will be mandated by law. Those who refuse will be hauled into court, warned, threatened, persecuted, and prosecuted, but we can rest assured that the Lord will not leave us or forsake us at that time.

Matt.10:18-20 says this "You shall be brought before governors and kings for my sake, for a testimony against them and the Gentiles. But when they deliver you up, take no thought how or what you shall speak: for it shall be given you in that same hour what you shall speak. It is not you that speak, but the Spirit of your father which speaks in you."

It's quite possible that believers who oppose the antichrist by refusing to take the "mark" during the tribulation will be threatened, arrested, tried, imprisoned, and at some point given **10 days to change their mind** before their head is removed.

Beheading is the method of execution that the antichrist will choose. **Rev.20: 4** John saw the souls of them that were **beheaded** for the witness of Jesus and for the word of God, and which had **not** worshipped the beast or his image.

They had not received his mark upon their foreheads or in their hand; they lived and reigned with Christ a thousand years.

Rev. 2: 10 says this: "Fear none of those things which you shall suffer; behold the devil shall cast some of you into prison that you may be tried, and **you shall have tribulation 10 days: be faithful unto death, and I will give you a crown of life.**"

If these martyrs came out of the great tribulation, then guess what, they must have been in it. The rapture is not yet, neither is the wrath of God, but it's getting closer.

The first 3 ½ years of tribulation is not the wrath of God but the wrath of the antichrist as he attempts to destroy anyone who stands in the way of his "One World Order." His goal is to be the king of all the kingdoms of the world. He would be a counterfeit king of kings.

Rev.13: 18 the number of the beast, 666, is not sufficient to number all of earth's population, so it might be the antichrist's personal number. (It is the number of a man)

If the international products code is somehow used to mark all of earth people there would be plenty of numbers available to identify the entire population of the world.

Some say that the international products code has 3 bars that are identical; the bar on each end, and the one in the very middle. They say these 3 bars are equal, each to the power of six. In spite of my diligent research I have not been able to prove or disprove this theory.

Keep in mind that while the antichrist is putting more and more pressure on society, he is being opposed for 3 ½ years by the two witnesses. The world is in a quandary as to whom to give their loyalty; this antichrist (answer man) or these two powerful men of God.

The two witnesses were killed in Ch.11 but their ministry will be for the entire first 3 ½ years of the tribulation. It's very likely that far more people will be lead to the Lord during these 3 ½ years of worldwide preaching than any other 3 ½ year period in history.

The missionaries do a wonderful job but they will never have a bully pulpit to oppose the antichrist like these two witnesses will have (with all the media coverage). Nor will they have such a pulpit of power as these two witnesses will have to preach the gospel around the world.

It is logical to think that the rapture of believers would take place after the 3 ½ years of worldwide preaching by these two witnesses so that new converts could be included in the rapture. This would put the rapture in the middle of the 7 years of tribulation.

REVELATION Chapter 14 A The "Wave" Offering,
First 3 ½ years *Interlude between 6th and 7th Seal*

Rev.14: 1 John sees a Lamb standing on Mt. Zion with 144,000 Jewish believers who have the Father's name written in their foreheads.

These are the same 144,000 who were sealed in their foreheads in chapter 7. There were 12,000 from each of the 12 tribes of Israel. *Rev.7: 3, 4*

The 144,000 are "true Jews" having no gentile blood mixed into them through inter-marriage and therefore **as believers,** qualify to be the **first fruits** unto God and the Lamb.

Romans 1:16 tells us that the power of God is unto salvation to everyone that believes: to the **Jew first,** and also to the Greek. (Gentile)

The 144,000 Jews represent the truly identifiable Jewish nation of Israel. It is they who must recognize Jesus as their Messiah; and due to the preaching of the two witnesses and the powerful ensuing earthquake Ch.11:13 they will begin to praise, and glorify the God of heaven in this future scenario.

God first targeted His chosen people for redemption beginning with the faith of Abraham. Eventually, after many centuries and generations, the Jewish people rejected and crucified their Messiah. Because they rejected Jesus as their Savior and redeemer, the grace of God was spread abroad to the Gentiles.

Nevertheless, Romans 1:16 reminds us that the power of God is unto salvation to everyone that believes: to the **Jew first,** and also to the Greek. (Gentile)

It might be that the main harvest of the earth, (The rapture of believers) composed primarily of Gentiles, can not happen until the 144,000 Jews **(first fruits)** have accepted Jesus as their Messiah and are presented to God the Father for His approval by Jesus Christ our high priest.

Lev. 23: 9-11 says: The Lord spoke unto Moses saying, speak unto the children of Israel, and say to them, when ye be come into the land which I give unto you, and shall reap the harvest thereof, then ye shall **bring a sheaf** (a bundle) of the **first fruits** of your harvest unto the priest: and he shall "**wave**" the sheaf before the Lord, to be accepted for you.

There's an old time Christian hymn that's based on *Lev.23: 9-11 "Bringing in the Sheaves, bringing in the Sheaves, we shall come rejoicing, bringing in the Sheaves."*

The 144,000 could be the *first fruits* just like the "**Wave offering**" without spot or blemish and without fault before the throne of God; just as the bride of Christ must be. *(Eph.5: 27)*

Therefore it might be that the main harvest of the earth, (The rapture of believers) composed primarily of Gentiles, can not happen until the 144,000 Jews (**first fruits**) have accepted Jesus as their Messiah and are presented to God the Father for His approval by Jesus Christ our High Priest.

When the earth is harvested, it might be that the 144,000 Jews must be presented to God, and approved by God before the Gentiles can be.

Rev.14: 4, 5 The 144,000 Jews were redeemed from among men by the blood of the Lamb. In their mouth was found no guile, they were without fault before the throne of God. (They passed inspection).

The 144,000 Jews are the **first fruit** unto God, but the church (body of Christ) is the **main harvest.** The rapture of the church is comprised mostly of Gentiles.

When the 144,000 have accepted Jesus as their Messiah they will be presented to God and approved by God, in this future scenario, then the main harvest (the rapture) of all other believers can happen.

Could it be that the Divine harvest of the earth will be accomplished in the same three steps that the fields of Boaz were harvested in the book of Ruth.

Step # 1. *The first fruits were presented by the high priest before God as a "Wave offering" for His approval. Lev.23: 9-11.* When the time comes for Jesus to harvest the earth the 144,000 Jews (the first fruits) could be that "Wave offering".

***Step # 2.** Then approval is given to reap the main harvest.* Then true believers in Jesus Christ worldwide, comprised mostly of Gentiles, will be the main harvest.

***Step # 3.** The gleaning of the four corners of the field.* Leviticus 23:22 says: When ye reap the harvest of your land, thou shalt not make a clean riddance of the corners of thy field when thou reapest, neither shalt thou gather any gleaning of thy harvest: thou shalt leave them unto the poor, and to the stranger: I am the Lord your God.

The survivors of the great tribulation who did not receive the mark of the beast might represent the four corners of the field (the world) left to be harvested. Many of them will be led to the Lord (gleaned) by the redeemed priests of God who will reign with Jesus for 1000 years. Rev.20: 6.

Just as Ruth worked in the field of Boaz and gleaned the four corners; we as the bride of Christ will continue to work in the four corners of the earth to harvest as many as possible for our Lord and Savior during the millennial reign of Christ. Satan will be bound at that time.

But this is a future scenario. As of Rev.14:12 the rapture of the saints has **not** yet occurred. There is still time for anyone who has not willingly taken the mark of the beast, to repent of their sins and ask Jesus Christ to come into their heart and save their soul.

Because the Jews rejected Jesus, their Messiah 2000 years ago, God spread His grace abroad to the Gentiles. This time of grace in which we now live is called the church age.

The church age will end with the fullness of the Gentiles, Rom.11:25, when the last Gentile is saved, just prior to ….. ***The rapture of believers.***

REVELATION   Chapter 14 B   The Harvest of the Earth is Ripe
First 3 ½ years   between 6th and 7th seal   The Rapture Chapter

Rev. 14: 14 John sees one like the Son of man (Jesus) wearing a gold crown and sitting **on a cloud**, (In the rapture Jesus meets us in the air). In His hand He has a sharp sickle. Sickles are used for harvesting.

Rev. 14:15, 16 An angel cries with a loud voice "Thrust in thy sickle, and reap: for the time is come for thee to reap; for ***the harvest of the earth is ripe***", and He thrust it in.

This may be Jesus gathering to Himself the people of God.

I I Thess. 2: 1 Now we beseech (urge) you brethren, by ***the coming of our Lord Jesus*** Christ, ***and by our gathering together unto Him*** that ye be not soon shaken in mind.

This strongly implies, the rapture of believers; when Jesus meets us in the air.

The bible never actually uses the word rapture. Maybe a better word would be removal, or rescue, or catching away, but they all imply the same thing. **~ The rapid removal of believers! ~**

I Thessalonians 4:16, 17 tells us that the Lord Himself shall descend from heaven with a shout, with the voice of the archangel, and with the trump of God: and *the dead in Christ shall rise first:* Then we which are alive and remain shall be caught up together with them *in the air*: and so shall we ever be with the Lord.

This is the middle of the 7 years of tribulation, just before the seventh seal is opened which begins the wrath of God on an unrepentant world. For 3 ½ years the antichrist has been forcing people to take the mark or die, He has broken the 7 year peace treaty with the Jews, killed the two witnesses, martyred millions of the saints of God, hijacked the temple, and exalted himself as God. ***The anger of God is beyond hot at this time.***

This is likely to be the time when believers in Jesus Christ are removed from harms way in a moment, in a twinkling of an eye so that the Wrath of God can begin as the seventh seal is opened.

I Corin. 15:51-53 Behold, I show you a mystery; we shall not all sleep, but we shall all be changed, in a moment, in a twinkling of an eye, at the last trump: for the trumpet shall sound, and the dead shall be raised incorruptible, and we shall be changed. For this corruptible must put on incorruption, and this mortal must put on immortality.

Verse 54, 55 So when this corruptible shall have put on incorruption, and this mortal shall have put on immortality, then shall be brought to pass the saying that is written, Death is swallowed up in victory. O death, where is thy sting? O grave, where is thy victory?

Noah's family was removed from harms way just before the flood of God's judgment.

Lot's family was removed just before God judged Sodom and Gomorrah. Believers will be removed from harms way just before God's wrath is poured on this wicked world.

***"Revelation 14: 14 thru 16"** The harvesting or gathering of the ripened earth by Jesus Christ himself* is seldom ever mentioned as a possible time for the rapture to occur and yet the likelihood of it occurring at that time is very high, and very logical. What else could these verses be referring to if not the "Return of Christ and the gathering of believers?"

~~~~~~

14: 17 Another angel came out of the temple of heaven also having a sickle. The first reaper with a sickle, which was Jesus, harvested good wheat (Believers) but the second reaper will harvest the grapes of wrath. (Unbelievers)

14: 19 The angel from the altar is saying "Gather the clusters of the vine of the earth, for her grapes are fully ripe, and cast them into the great wine press of the wrath of God." (These are the grapes of wrath spoken of in Joel 3:13).

Joel 3:13 says: Put ye in the sickle, for the harvest is ripe: come, get you down; for the press is full, the vats overflow; for their wickedness is great.

14:20 "They were trampled in the winepress outside the city". Where was Jesus crucified? Jesus was crucified outside of the city of Jerusalem.

Not wine, but blood came from these grapes because these are the grapes of the wrath of God. These are actual people who have blasphemed God and rejected His grace and mercy time and time again.

They were given **one last chance to repent** just before the rapture occurred, as the angel in Rev.14: 6 flew around the world preaching the everlasting gospel unto every nation, kindred, tongue, and people. (Many repented, many did not)

The Gospel will be preached around the world in three different ways as we draw near to the end. **1.** Christians are commanded to Go into all the world and preach the gospel to every creature. *Mark 16:15.* **2.** God will send two powerful witnesses who will stand before all the earth to preach and prophecy for the first 3 ½ years of the tribulation. *Rev.11:3.* **3.** An angel will fly around the world preaching the everlasting gospel to every nation, kindred, tongue, and people. *Rev.14: 6.*

God is not willing that any should parish. He goes to great lengths to save as many as possible. What a wonderful Savior He is.

We've been studying the rapture of the church. ***The purpose of the rapture is to remove believers from harms way*** so God can exact revenge and punishment on those who have harmed His people.

The rapture is the same thing as the first resurrection. There is **no** difference. If there were a difference, then they would be two major resurrections happening almost back to back; within 7 years of each other because scripture places both of them just before the millennial reign of Christ. It makes more sense that they are not two events, but one.

With the powerful preaching of the two anointed witnesses in chapter 11, isn't it more logical that God would simply wait 3 ½ more years to include all new converts?

With the saints safely removed from harms way, God will ***begin*** to pour out His wrath in the last 3 ½ years of the great tribulation with the opening of the 7th Seal. The 7th seal contains the 7 trumpets, the 7 bowls judgment, followed by the battle of Armageddon.

Everything we have studied so far has happened in the first 3 ½ years. The second 3 ½ years are all contained in *Ch.8, 9, and 15-18.*

An interesting thing about our study of the first 3 ½ years of the tribulation is that two of the first 14 chapters don't seem to belong in the first 3 ½ years. They are Chapters 8 and 9. They clearly speak of the wrath of God which occurs in the second 3 ½ years.

Therefore, chapters 8 and 9 probably should have been placed after chapter 14 and before chapter 15.

Chapters 8 and 9 are the main two chapters that prevent the book of Revelation from being in chronological order. The chart below shows where chapters 8 and 9 should have been placed.

```
                        Rapture
First 3 ½ years = tribulation.     ! Second 3 ½ years = Wrath of God.
                                   !
Chapters 1, ----- 7,    v   10, -----14, !  ^  Ch.15 -----18
                        v                ^
                        Ch. 8, 9, _ _ _  ^
```

The problem isn't how chapters 8 & 9 were written (There is nothing wrong with the content) but how they were arranged when King James ordered the KJV of the bible to be published.

Honorable men did their best to arrange the chapters and verses the way they thought they should be but some chapters and verses, especially in the book of Romans, were divided in controversial ways, because the apostle Paul used such long sentences. Many of his sentences were more like paragraphs. So it was difficult to know were to stop one verse and start the next. So they did the best they could and usually got it right.

These are the same scholars who inserted italics wherever they thought it might be helpful. But Revelation is a complicated book and I think their placement of chapters 8 & 9 was incorrect.

They probably should have been placed between chapters 14 &15 because they clearly speak of the wrath of God which occurs in the last 3 ½ years. So the problem with chapters 8 & 9 has nothing to do with content, only the arrangement.

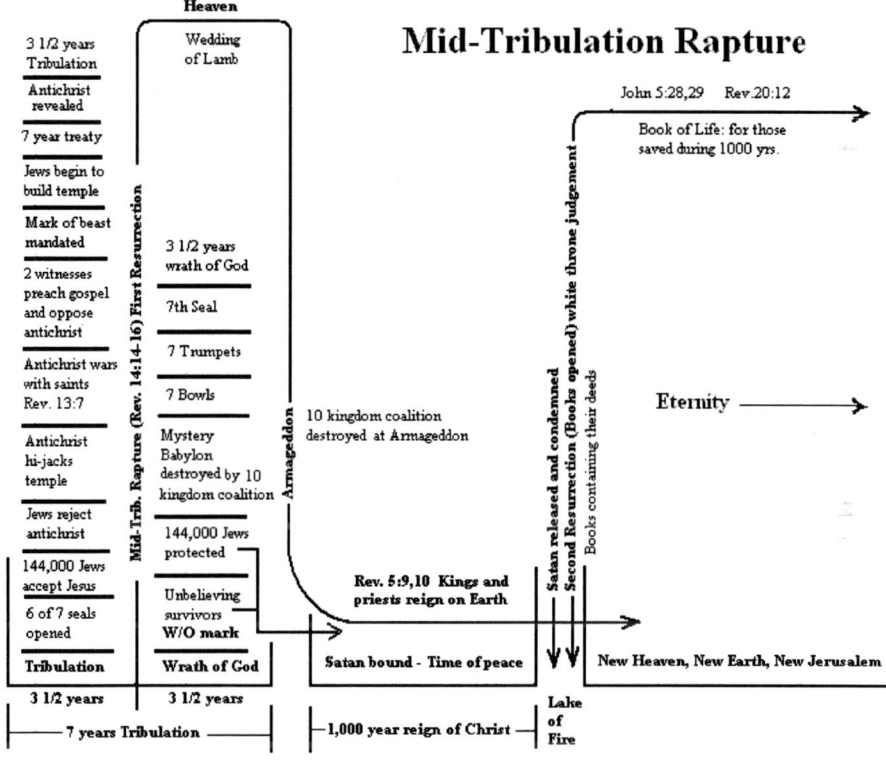

The first 3 ½ years of the 7 years of tribulation is basically the wrath of Satan poured out on all who oppose his *new world order*. The **new world order** is an evil world regime designed to destroy all opposition and ultimately exalt Satan, through his right hand man (the antichrist), as king of all the kingdoms of this world. He is a counterfeit to Jesus Christ "King of Kings and Lord of Lords."

True Christians differ on their views of pre, mid, and post tribulation rapture but regardless of which view we adopt; **how can we justify a rapture** of believers that occurs **just prior to the first resurrection** of believers mentioned in Rev.20: 4, 5, 6.

Is there any difference between the *rapture of believers* implied in I Thess.4:16, 17 and the *first resurrection of believers* mentioned in Rev. 20: 4, 5, 6 ?

Since the seven years of tribulation (which includes the rapture) occurs just before the millennium, and the first resurrection also occurs just before the millennium; that would put the rapture and the first resurrection within 7 years of being back to back with each other. What would be the point of that?

However, it would possibly make sense if *the rapture* of believers *and the first resurrection* of believers *are the same thing.*

We must keep in mind that the rapture, by itself, is a huge resurrection in that the dead in Christ shall **rise first.** Therefore, Rev. 20: 6 might be referring to the rapture when it says, "Blessed and holy is he that has part in *the first resurrection (the rapture),* and on such the second death has no power."

But if the rapture and the first resurrection are two different occurrences, then they are within 7 years of each other, and the second one could only include people saved during the 7 years of tribulation. The question is ……..

Who is left that could lead them to the Lord during the tribulation? And if somehow they did invite Jesus into their heart; then the faith of these new believers would have to be so strongly developed that they would be the source of all the millions of martyrs mentioned through out the 7 years of tribulation. What is the likelihood of that happening? Not much!

They would also be present during the undiluted wrath of God during the last 3 ½ years of tribulation. Romans 5: 9, I Thess. 5: 9 tell us believers are not subject to God's wrath.

The only logical conclusion is that **the rapture of believers** and **the first resurrection of believers are the same thing.** They happen at mid-tribulation and all of God's faithful will be out of harms way before the wrath of God begins in the second 3 ½ years.

The second 3 ½ years of the great tribulation will be God pouring out His undiluted wrath on the kingdoms of the antichrist, and the unrepentant reprobates who have rebelled against God, and harmed or destroyed His people.

After the battle of Armageddon will be the establishment of a peaceful earthly kingdom where Jesus Christ will rule and reign from Jerusalem with His saints for 1000 years.

Then will be the great White Throne judgment (the second resurrection) which is primarily for the lost, but not exclusively. Many human survivors of the 7 years of tribulation will be led to the Lord during the 1000 year reign of Jesus Christ. They will be led to the Lord by the redeemed priests of God who are mentioned in *Rev.20: 6,* and *Rev.5: 9, 10.*

Then the great White Throne judgment will be followed by a New Heaven, a New Earth, and a New Jerusalem where believing saints (as the bride of Christ) will live forever. Amen.

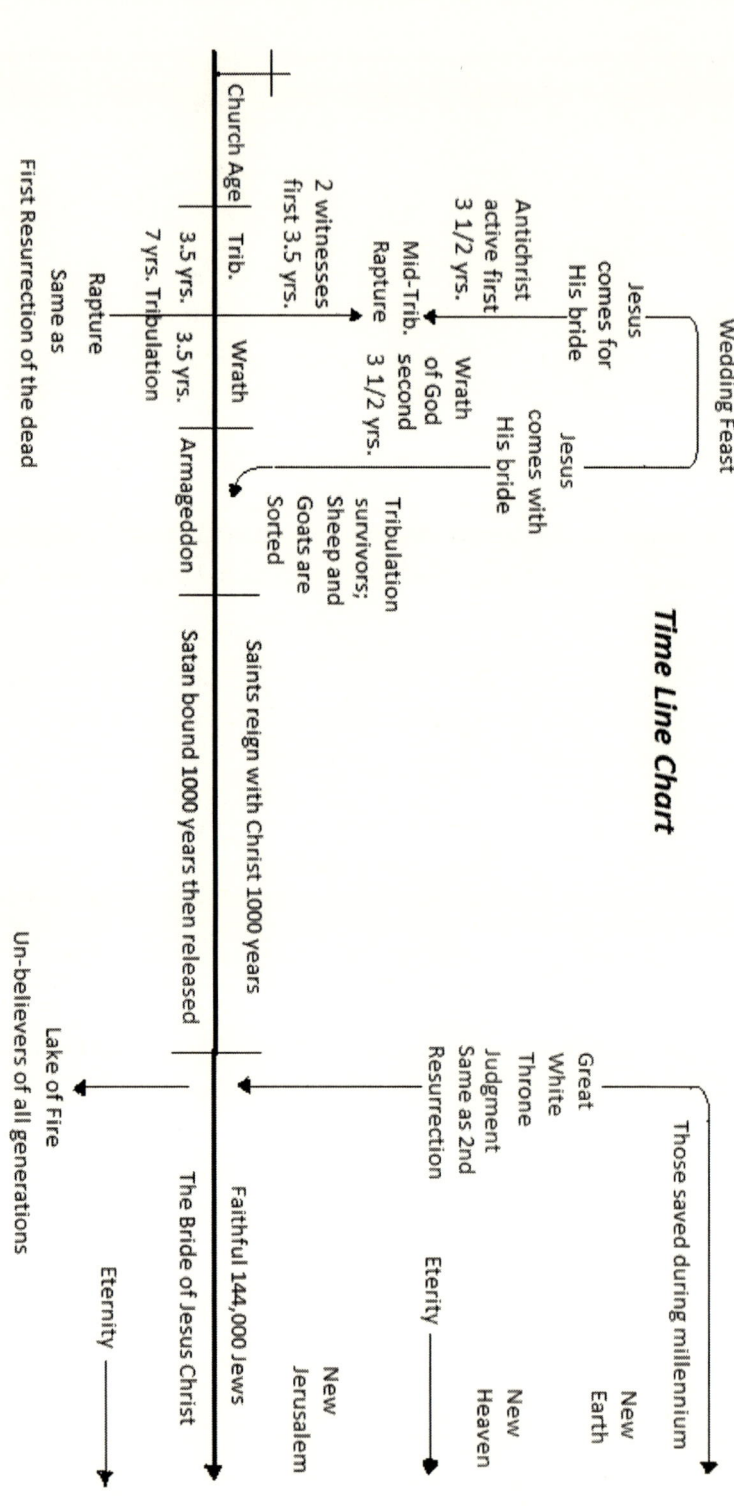

Part Two

~ Second ~

3 ½ Years of Seven

THE WRATH
~ OF GOD ~

REVELATION   Chapter 8   Seventh Seal Opened
Last 3 ½ year   *The Wrath of God*   Seven Trumpets Sound

The first 6 seals of judgment occur in the first 3 ½ years. After a long interlude the seventh, which is the last seal of judgment, occurs in the second 3 ½ years.

The 7th seal unleashes two more series of seven judgments, the trumpets and the bowls.

The trumpets and the bowls both occur in the last 3 ½ years of the great tribulation.

No trace of **Gentile Christians** will be found on earth during the last 3 ½ years of the tribulation. *(Chapters 8, 9, 15, 16, 17, 18)*

God has mercifully removed them (via the rapture) out of harms way, (at mid trib. *Rev.14:14-16*), just before God's wrath comes down on ***those left behind.***

Keep in mind that Christians are **not** subject to the wrath of God because we are at peace with God. Rom.5: 9, Rom.8:1, and I Thess. 5: 9

Genesis Ch.18 Abraham asked the angel if God would spare the city of Sodom if there were 50 righteous people there and the angel said "yes". Then he asked about 45, 30, 20, and 10, but what if he would have gone down to one? Do you think God would have spared Sodom for the sake of one righteous person?

The answer is "yes" so God had to remove or protect every last one of them because God's people are not subject to the wrath of God.

Christians **are** subject to tribulation. Even Jesus said, "In this world you will have tribulation; but be of good cheer, I have overcome the world." *John 16:33*

Christians **are** present during the first 3 ½ years of tribulations.

How else could the antichrist make war with them and overcome them. (Rev.13: 7)

Now our study of the first 3 ½ years is finished, and we are about to begin our study of the second 3 ½ years. Revelation is **not** necessarily written in chronological order.

To begin the second 3 ½ years we must go to chapters 8, 9, and then 15-18

Rev. 8: 1 When the Lamb of God opened the 7th seal, there was silence in heaven for about a half of an hour. Why?

This is a very somber and sobering moment of time to assess the devastation, terror, and horrible judgment that is about to begin on the rebellious, reprobates *left behind* on earth.

This is not a time of rehabilitation, restoration, or regeneration. This is the time of God's undiluted wrath on those who have already made their decision to reject the grace and mercy of Jesus Christ.

God is no longer interested in saving these people. They have already closed their minds and their hearts. Their conscience has been seared with a hot iron.

Rev. 8: 2, 3 John sees seven angels standing before God holding seven trumpets, and before any of them begin to blow, another angel stood at the altar of God having a golden censer.

This angel was given much incense (Sweet fragrance) to offer with the prayers of the saints on the altar which was before the throne of God. God remembers the prayers of the saints throughout the generations, as they pleaded for God's justice and revenge.

Rev. 8: 4, 5 The angel filled the censer (measuring device) with fire from the altar and cast it into the earth.

Rev. 8: 6, 7 The **first trumpet** was blown and there was **hail and fire, mingled with blood**, cast upon the earth and **1/3 of the trees** and grass were burned up.

Rev.12:12-14 Tell us the woman (Unsaved Israel, and the 144,000 believing

Jews) still on earth after the rapture of the saints are protected for the last 3 ½ years of great tribulation while God brings His undiluted wrath on this wretched world. God will take care of His people.

Rev. 8: 8, 9 The **second trumpet** sounded and **"a" great mountain burning with fire** was cast into the sea and 1/3 of the sea became blood, 1/3 of sea life died, and 1/3 of the ships were destroyed.

A great mountain burning sounds like it could be an active volcano but it's not likely that this is a volcano that blew its top because the massive destruction spoken of here (1/3 of the sea) is more than any **one** volcano could produce. (Earth's surface is more than 3/5 water)

Something the size of a mountain falling from the sky and being on fire could be an asteroid or meteor from outer space, **or** possibly a fire brand from the prayer altar that is before the throne of God.

Here again we have a fire and blood mixture that may have originated from God's altar of the prayers of the saints who were martyred. *(Rev.8: 5)*

Rev. 8: 10, 11 The **third trumpet** sounded and there fell a **great burning star** from heaven named "Wormwood". **It made 1/3 of the fresh water bitter.** Many people died due to the bitter water. "Wormwood" means bitterness.

Here again we have **fire falling down from heaven**. This fire may have originated straight from the altar of the prayers of the saints who were martyred.

Rom.12:19, 20 says "Avenge not yourselves, but rather give place to wrath: for it is written, vengeance is mine; I will repay, says the Lord." If your enemy hungers, feed him, if he thirst, give him to drink; for in so doing you will heap coals of fire on his head............. It's very possible that *these are those coals!*

Rev. 8: 12 The **fourth trumpet** sounded and **one third of the sun, moon, stars,** and **earth** were **darkened.** A celestial phenomenon is happening.

The size of the sun in relation to the earth is like a basketball beside a garden pea. They are 93,000,000 miles apart. What would it take to darken the sun alone by one third?

One third of the sun could be darkened if one third of the light were somehow blocked from reaching the earth. (That could happen)

To block one third of the light of the sun, moon, and stars from the earth there would have to be something massive happening in the celestial heavens such as a thick cloud of meteorites or asteroid like objects between the sun and the earth.

Some would have to be large enough to look like a burning mountain as it fell into the sea and destroyed one third of the marine life. This would be consistent with the second trumpet judgment.

If there were enough of them coming toward the earth they could reduce the light of the sun, moon, stars, and the amount of sunshine on earth by one third.

Most of them would no doubt miss the earth or burn up in the earth's atmosphere, but plenty of them would hit and cause great devastation.

The source of these fire brands could be a celestial phenomenon **or** they could come straight from the prayer altar that is before the throne of God. It contains the prayers of the saints that have been martyred as well as other saints who have been wronged.

Think how terrifying it will be in the day of God's wrath when people can be hit at any time, day or night by something big or small entering from outer space.

Believers don't have to worry about this because we are at peace with God. We are not subject to the wrath of God.

But why would there even be an altar in heaven? Typically an altar is a place where animals are killed and sacrificed. Why would sacrifices be necessary in heaven?

Sacrifices would **not** need to be made in heaven. These sacrifices were already made on earth by these saints who had been persecuted through out the ages. But their prayers for God to avenge their enemies are stored up against the day of God's wrath. They are stored in the altar that is before the throne of God.

REVELATION Chapter 9   Demons from bottomless
Last 3 ½ years   *The Wrath of God*   pit, and Euphrates River

Rev.9: 1 The fifth trumpet sounded and John sees a **star** fall from heaven to earth and to **him** was given the key to the bottomless pit. (The Abyss)

We know that the **star** was a person by the personal pronoun **"him"**.

Satan is described as a falling star. Luke 10:18 Jesus said "I beheld Satan as lightning fall from heaven.

Rev. 9: 2 Satan opened the bottomless pit and smoke came out **like** the smoke of a great furnace, enough to darken the sun and the sky. (Like millions of bats out of a cave)

Rev. 9: 3, 4 Out of the smoke came locusts. The locusts were told **not** to hurt any green thing, only those men who had **not** the seal of God in their forehead. Locust (insects) could not make that distinction, but demons could.

These are obviously **not** normal locusts that eat every green thing in sight. They are very likely to be demons from the pit of hell.

These demons are forbidden to hurt anyone who has the seal of God in their forehead. Rev.7: 3, 4 informed us that 12,000 Jews were sealed in their foreheads from each of the twelve tribes of Israel. This would imply that these 144,000 Jews are still on earth after the rapture of the church, but they are being protected by God.

We are **now** studying the second 3 ½ years of tribulation. No trace of the believing **Gentile** church can be found in chapters 8 or 9, because they are safely with the Lord in heaven. Yet the 144,000 Jewish believers are still present on the earth.

By God's design, the 144,000 may have missed the rapture because Gentile believers are God's spiritually chosen people, while the Jews are God's earthly chosen people. God chose the Jewish bloodline to bring Jesus into the world, but **All believers** will end up together on the new earth, eventually, with Jesus Christ our Lord.

It might be that God has left the 144,000 faithful Jews on earth during the last 3 ½ years of the great tribulation to witness to their fellow Jews about Jesus while they are being protected and fed in the wilderness hideout. *Rev.12: 6*

I doubt that the Jewish believers remain on earth to witness to the whole world because they have already done that in the first 3 ½ years through the two anointed witnesses in Ch.11.

When the antichrist killed the two witnesses and hijacked their newly finished temple the Jews were force to flee into **a** wilderness hideout were God protects and nourishes them for the last 3 ½ years of the great tribulation. *Rev.12: 6, Matt.24:15-22*

So, it's not likely that the Jewish believers remain on earth after the rapture to witness to the whole world. It's more likely that they will witnesses only to their own.

Rev. 9: 5, 6 God has allowed Satan to release these hideous demons to mercilessly torment those who showed no mercy to their fellow man.

Matt. 5: 7 "Blessed are the merciful for they shall be shown mercy." The opposite is also true. Cursed are the merciless for they shall be shown **no** mercy.

God shows these people **no** mercy, they desire to die, and death flees from them. Perhaps these are the people responsible for the deaths of those under the altar. *(Rev. 6: 9, 10)*

Rev. 9: 7-10 Getting into the description of these demons is probably not necessary. It suffices that they are evil angels. Clearly they are battle hardened warriors that we must never underestimate.

Eph. 6:12 says "We wrestle not against flesh and blood, but against principalities, against powers, against the rulers of the darkness of this world, and against spiritual wickedness in high places."

The way to oppose demons and devils is to rebuke them by the word of God, bind them in the name of Jesus, resist them and they will flee from you.

Rev. 9:11 The fact that they have a king could imply they have a rank and file system. They are well organized and have "a chain of command".

Rev. 9:13 -15 The sixth trumpet sounds and the angel is told to loose the four angels that are bound in the river Euphrates.

Four angels were loosed which were prepared for an exact moment in time. In reverse order: (a year, a month, a day, an hour) to slay 1/3 of the earth's population.

The timing on the slaughter of **one third** of earth's population is so exact that it's likely to be a nuclear exchange happening in diverse places around the world. *Zechariah 14:12.* Believers should not be frightened by this because God will have already removed them from harms way via the rapture. *Rev.14: 14-16*

Rev. 9:16 The huge number of this army of horsemen (200,000,000) tells us that in a day of modern warfare, actual horsemen would not be used or capable of killing one third of the people of the earth. These are more likely to be another batch of demons.

These Euphrates River demons are a more deadly batch than the bottomless pit demons. God is allowing them to be released to torment and kill people in His wrath.

Rev. 9:20, 21 The rest of the people who were not killed by these plagues repented not.

They displayed no remorse, regret, or repentance for anything they have said or done. They are truly diabolical and reprobate.

Chapter 15 is next in the order of events in the last 3 ½ years of the great tribulation.

SONG OF MOSES

REVELATION   Chapter 15   Prelude to Seven Bowls Judgment
Last 3 ½ Years   *The Wrath of God*

Rev. 15: 1, 2 John sees a marvelous sign in heaven; seven angels having the last seven plagues. They are filled with the wrath of God.

He also sees a sea of glass which we learned earlier was before the throne of God. John describes it as being clear as crystal. *(Rev.4: 6)*

However, now it is mixed with fire. Perhaps it is reflecting God's fury at this time. Remember this is the time of God's wrath upon the wicked.

John also sees the martyrs that had gotten the victory over the beast, his image, his mark, and over the number of his name. How can a person be murdered by the antichrist and still be victorious?

They have the victory because they did not obey the beast, or worship his image, or receive his mark, and because they will experience eternal life with Jesus Christ their Savior.

15: 3 They were standing on the sea of glass and each had a harp. They were inspired to sing the song of Moses and the song of the Lamb.

The song of Moses in *Exodus 15: 1-18* was a song of **glorious triumph** over their enemies and the faithful deliverance by the Lord from the bondage of Egypt.

The lyrics were that of worship; they were singing great and marvelous are your works, just and true are your ways, Oh King of saints.

Rev. 15: 6, 7 The seven angels came out of the temple holding the seven plagues. Do you remember who the four beasts are? We learned earlier in *(Rev.4: 8) (Isaiah 6: 2, 3)* they are Seraphim angels. One of these 4 Seraphim gave unto the seven angels, seven golden bowls filled with the wrath of God.

Rev. 15: 8 The temple was filled with smoke from the glory of God and from His power.

God's anger is beyond hot at this time. He is filled with righteous indignation toward those who have shaken their puny fist in God's face and blasphemed His Holy name.

He has been patient and long suffering. He has been kind and sacrificial, even giving up His life on a cruel cross. He has used every method available to seek and to save as many as possible. But this is an evil and adulteress generation, a generation of vipers. What more could God do than what He has already done to save as many as possible?

REVELATION
Last 3 ½ years   Chapter 16   Seven Bowls Judgment
Undiluted Wrath of God

Rev. 16: 1 John hears a great voice out of the temple saying to the seven angels "Go your ways, pour out the bowls of the wrath of God upon the earth."

The voice John heard from the temple could only be that of God Himself, because the last verse of the last chapter said, "no one else was allowed to be in the temple of God until the seven plagues were fulfilled." That is: until God's anger is satisfied.

God is about to systematically disassemble the 10 kingdom coalition that the un-holy trinity has set up so that the antichrist could be the king of all the kings and kingdom of the world.

Rev. 16: 2 The **first** angel poured out his **bowl** and there were ugly, **painful sores** on those who had the mark of the beast and worshiped his image. It's almost as if they were marked in their foreheads for destruction; while the 144,000 Jews were marked in their foreheads for preservation. *Ch.7*

Rev. 16: 3 The **second** angel poured out his **bowl** upon the **sea** and it **became as the blood** of a dead man. Every living thing in the sea died.

Rev. 16: 4 The **third** angel poured out his **bowl** on the **rivers** and **springs** and they **became blood.** That doesn't leave very much fresh water to drink.

Rev. 16: 5-7 John hears the angel in charge of the waters say, "You are righteous Lord, because of your judgments, they have shed the blood of saints and prophets and you have given them blood to drink."

What goes around comes around. They were cruel and blood thirsty people; so now, blood is just about all they have to drink. There's a parallel passage in *Isaiah 49:26*.

Isaiah 49:26 says "I will feed them that oppress thee (God's people) with their own flesh; and they shall be drunken with their own blood, as with sweet wine: and all flesh shall know that I the Lord am thy Savior and thy Redeemer, the mighty One of Jacob."

A person can only live a few days without water so we must assume that there is an available source of water.

In our study of Revelation chapter 11 verse 6 the two witnesses from God were given power to shut heaven that it rain not in the days of their prophecy. The days of their prophecy were the first 3 ½ years. So, in the first 3 ½ years of the tribulation there will probably be a worldwide drought.

If it rained not the first 3 ½ years of the 7 years of tribulation then it's likely there will be more than enough rain the second 3 ½ years to sustain life. So, rain will probably be their only source of drinking water.

Rev. 14:20 says the winepress was trodden without the city, and blood came out of the wine press, even unto the horse's bridles, by the space of a thousand and six hundred furlongs; which is about 180 miles at a depth of 4 ½ feet. Can you imagine this?

Most people think this happens at Armageddon; but I don't think so. It probably happens before Armageddon. With the seas, rivers, and streams turning to blood in Rev.16 verses 3 and 4, plus this enormous amount of rainfall in the second 3 ½ years, it's easy to see how this blood and water mixture could reach the level of a horse's bridle in some places for 180 miles.

However, I don't think it takes place in Israel because the entire length of Israel is only about 200 miles, and it probably happens before Armageddon because the heavy rainfall will stop before Armageddon starts. We know this because of the next bowl judgment.

Rev. 16: 8, 9 The **forth** angel poured out his **bowl upon the sun** and fire was given to him to **scorch men with fire.** Undoubtedly the rains will have stopped at this time.

Even while being scorched with great heat, which no doubt causes them to blister, they blasphemed the name of God who had power over the plagues.

Rev. 16: 10, 11 The **fifth** angel poured out his **bowl** on **the throne of the beast** and his kingdom was **full of darkness**. They gnawed their tongues for pain.

John 3:19 says this: And this is the condemnation, that light is come into the world, and men loved darkness rather than light, because their deeds were evil. Those who loved darkness more than light get more darkness than they bargained for.

Rev. 16: 12 The **sixth** angel poured out his **bowl** on the river **Euphrates** and the water was **dried up** that the way of the kings of the east might be prepared. The Euphrates River will probably be a mixture of blood and water at that time but it will still dry up.

The Euphrates River is a natural barrier to any ground attack from the east against Israel. The sixth bowl judgment would provide a dried up river bed by which huge armies could move westward to attack Israel. These would be land forces attacking from the east.

That seems like primitive combat for this day of modern warfare, but keep in mind that all of this happens after the world has been absolutely devastated by the 7 seals, 7 trumpets, and the 7 bowls, not to mention a possible nuclear war. *See: Zech.14:12*

What is happening is that God is gathering the 10 king coalition and their armies to fight this huge battle of Armageddon Rev.19:19.

This huge 10 kingdom coalition headed up by the "unholy trinity" (Satan, antichrist, and the false prophet) will attempt to eliminate the Jewish people once and for all. They will think of it as "The final solution."

Their ultimate goal is to drive Israel into the Mediterranean Sea by attacking from the east crossing the dried up Euphrates River and moving westward.

Satan's ultimate goal is to eliminate the Jewish people so that God will never be able to fulfill that most important Old Testament prophecy. **Ezekiel 37: 27-28** *My tabernacle also shall be with them: Yea, I will be their God, and they* *shall be my people. And the heathen shall know that I the Lord do sanctify Israel, when my sanctuary shall be in the midst of them for evermore.*

Isaiah 55:11 God says "So shall my word be that goeth forth out of my mouth: it shall not return unto me void, but it shall accomplish that which I please, and it shall prosper in the thing whereto I sent it."

Satan knows scripture, so Satan knows that if he can keep God from fulfilling that prophecy, he has made God a liar like himself. God would no longer have the legal ability to condemn him to the lake of fire where he will be tormented day and night forever. *(Rev.20: 10)*

In this future scenario the Jews are no longer deceived as to whom their true Messiah is. Now Satan must make one last all out effort to destroy them at the battle of Armageddon. The Jews must be present on the earth during the battle of Armageddon for that to happen. The fact is, it will **not** happen because in Ch.19, God will prevent Satan's plan.

Readers must understand that Revelation chapters 16 and 17 both touch on information about the battle of Armageddon but the actual battle does not occur until chapter 19 at the very end of the 7 years of tribulation.

REVELATION Chapter 16 B Armageddon and
Last 3 ½ years *The Wrath of God* The Great Earthquake

Rev. 16:13, 14 John sees three unclean spirits come out of the mouths of the dragon (Satan), the beast (antichrist), and the false prophet (antichrist's spokesman).

These three are the unholy trinity. Why the unclean spirits are like frogs is uncertain but it suffices to know that they are the spirits of devils.

They are the spirits of devils working miracles (Such as calling down fire from heaven *Rev.13:13* to impress the kings of the earth and the whole world; perhaps to convince them to unilaterally attack Israel. The purpose is to gather them to the battle of **that great day of God Almighty.** (Armageddon)

Rev. 16:15 Jesus himself interjects to say, "Behold, I come as a thief. Blessed is he that is watching and keeps his garment, (of righteousness) lest he walk naked, and they see his shame."

This might be why some people believe in post tribulation rapture, thinking that there are still Gentile Christians on earth and Jesus is addressing them at this time.

Although I respect their post tribulation view I find some problems with it. If there are still Gentile Christians on earth that have **not** been raptured at some earlier time, then they would be subjected to the undiluted wrath of God during the 7 trumpets, and the 7 bowls judgment. This would be unscriptural because Rom.5: 9, and I Thess. 5: 9 tell us that "believers are not subject to the wrath of God."

There is evidence to suggest that (The woman) Israel will be protected and nourished on earth during the second 3 ½ years of tribulation. *(Rev.12: 13, 14)*

However, I see no evidence to support that Gentile Christians are present and protected on earth during the 7 trumpets or the 7 bowls judgment. Both occur in the last 3 ½ years of tribulation. *(Ch.8, 9 and Ch.15 –18)*

It's more likely that Jesus' statement in *Rev.16:15* "Behold I come as a thief" is directed strictly to the remnant of Jews (the 144,000) as encouragement for them to keep their faith intact to the very end. Jesus will come quickly to rescue them from total annihilation at the battle of Armageddon.

Matt. 24:21, 22 "There shall be great tribulation such as was **not** since the beginning of the world to this time, no, nor ever shall be. And except those days be shortened, there should no flesh be saved: but for the **elect's** sake, those days will be shortened." The **elect** of God are the 144,000 Jews.

It's likely that the Jews are present on the earth during the 7 bowls judgment because their homeland is about to be attacked by the unholy trinity *and a huge global coalition of 10 kings with their armies at Armageddon. Rev.16: 13, 14*

Please notice the last line of Rev.16: 14. The battle is identified as "that Great Day of God Almighty." This battle belongs to the Lord, not to the spirit of devils.

Rev. 16:16 The KJV says "He" (God Almighty) gathered them to a place called in Hebrew, Armageddon. They think they gathered themselves there to destroy Israel. Actually it is God gathering these kings and their armies to Armageddon for their own destruction. This chapter does not describe the actual battle. That battle is best described in chapter 19.

Rev. 16:17, 18 The seventh angel poured out his bowl into the air and out of the temple of heaven came a great voice from the throne of God saying, **"IT IS DONE".**

What is done? The 7 seals, 7 trumpets, and now the 7 bowls judgment are all poured out.

This 7th bowl judgment poured into the air will send a message to the world that God is still in control. Even at this point of total devastation around the world, *God is Almighty.*

The 7th bowl judgment will also include lightning, rumbling, thunder, and a worldwide earthquake *much larger than any before.* This enormous earthquake, unlike the one in Revelation Chapter 6, **is** part of the wrath of

God. This powerful earthquake might be the one that causes the earth to reel to and fro like a drunkard as mentioned in Isaiah 24: 20. The earth will literally wobble on its axis.

REVELATION Chapter 17 A Mystery Babylon
Last 3 ½ Years *The Wrath of God*

Rev.17: 1, 2 One of the seven powerful angels that had the seven bowls offers to show John the judgment of the great harlot that sits on many waters. The seven bowls have already been poured out so we must assume that we could be looking back on earlier events.

The great harlot is the chief city of the dragon and the antichrist's evil world regime. It is the capital of the corrupt tribulation world system that viciously martyrs God's people. We are looking back on the capital city that existed until the seven bowls were poured out.

Rev. 17: 3 John is carried away, "in the spirit" meaning a spiritual state in which one receives divine revelation. John was carried into the wilderness; (a spiritually desolate place). He sees a woman sitting upon a scarlet beast which is supporting and carrying her. The beast is full of names of blasphemy.

This scarlet colored, blasphemous beast the woman is riding on has 7 heads and 10 horns just like the antichrist in Rev.13: 1.

The horns refer to kings or kingdoms according to Rev.17: 12 which says: The ten horns which thou sawest are ten kings, which have received no kingdom as yet; but receive power as kings one hour with the beast.

This sounds like they are **not** kings chosen by their countrymen but czars appointed by this world dictator. So the antichrist is the beast with 7 heads and 10 horns. He heads up the coalition of 10 kings that support the wicked city; the great harlot. She is probably supported with tax monies from the 10 kingdom coalition.

This coalition is comprised of 10 kings. Each kingdom will be composed of many countries. Each kingdom will answer to the antichrist as if he is the king of kings.

Dan.7: 8 says: I considered the horns and behold there came up among them another little horn before whom there were three of the first horns plucked up by the roots: and behold in this horn were eyes like the eyes of a man, and a mouth speaking great things.

The little horn **is** the antichrist that plucked up 3 of the first 10 horns (kings) temporarily reducing their total to 7 kings. However, Rev.17:12 -14 implies that the three kings who were plucked up will be replaced to bring the total back up to ten before the battle of Armageddon begins.

Rev.17: 12-14 (paraphrased) The ten horns which thou sawest are 10 kings. These have one mind and shall give their power and strength to the beast. These shall make war with the Lamb, and the Lamb shall overcome them: for He is Lord of lords, and King of kings: and they that are with Him are called, and chosen, and faithful, (The bride of Christ).

So the 10 kings will unilaterally agree to attack Israel. This battle will take place at Armageddon. The chosen and faithful mentioned here will return with Jesus as His bride.

The 3 kings were probably removed due to a lack of full compliance to the antichrist's one world agenda. But they will be replaced by 3 kings who will comply.

Rev. 17: 5 This wicked city has a name written on her forehead, MYSTERY BABYLON, MOTHER OF HARLETS, AND ABOMINATIONS OF THE EARTH.

Cities don't have foreheads but they do have reputations and this title is her legacy.

We can assume that the kingdom of the antichrist will have a headquarter city that will be revealed at that time. It may go by a different name than Babylon, but it will be the same wicked city. It will be the headquarters of the antichrist and will probably be located within the former Roman Empire.

Rev.17: 6 John is mesmerized by the sight of the woman, drunk on the blood of the saints, and the martyrs who remained faithful unto death. *How could she be so cold and cruel?* The fact is that more Christians have been martyred in the 20th century than in all of the previous 19 centuries combined.

Rev. 17: 7 The angel in John's heavenly vision offers to tell him the mystery of the woman and the beast with 7 heads and 10 horns on which she rides.

Rev. 17: 8 The mystery is that the beast carrying the woman **"was, is not, and yet is, and shall ascend out of the bottomless pit,** for a short time, and then go into perdition." (Doom)

The only things that come out of the bottomless pit are demons and devils. This devil has 7 heads and 10 horns, like the one in *Rev.13:1* that turned out to be the antichrist.

If indeed this beast is the antichrist, **or** part of the one world system that he heads up; then we can speculate as to **what world system "was, is not, and yet is."**

Rev.17: 9 historically, ancient Rome **"was"** famous for being situated on seven hills. Rome **was** the capital of the Roman Empire and had a world system that persecuted Christians at that time.

It would seem that **the Roman Empire** has not existed for many centuries. However, if it does exist in a dormant state waiting for an opportune time to rise up again, then it would be a world empire that **"was, is not, and yet is."**

The Roman Empire was (in Jesus' days), **is not** (for many centuries, including now), **and yet is** (poised to rise again in the great tribulation) headed up by the antichrist and his coalition of ten evil kings.

Ten evil kings who rule over 10 kingdoms around the world are all core groups loyal to the antichrist and strongly opposed to anyone who did **not** take the mark of the beast. They are more than willing to "rid the world" of those who refuse to take the mark of the beast and be part of the new one world order. The **"One World Order"** of the antichrist is a counter balance to the "one world order" of the millennial reign of Jesus Christ.

Mystery Babylon, the Harlot, the 10 kingdom coalition, the One World agenda, and the revived Roman Empire are all the same united system that will be headed up by the antichrist as he attempts to form his "One World Order" with him as king of all kings.

REVELATION   Chapter 17 B   Mystery Babylon
Last 3 ½ years   *The Wrath of God*

Rev.17: verse 9 says: Here is the mind that has wisdom; giving us fair warning that what is coming up in the next few verses is very challenging.

Rev.17: 10, 11 say this: There are seven kings: **five are fallen**, and **one is**, and **the other is not yet come**; and when he cometh, he must continue a short space. And the beast that was, and is not, even he is the eighth, and is of the seven, and goeth into perdition.

So, *Rev.17: 10, 11* speak of the 7 kings (empires), of which 5 are fallen.

What 5 world empires do we know of historically that have fallen? (1). Ancient Egypt, (2). Assyria, (3). Babylon, (4). Media-Persia, and (5). Greece. These are five world empires that have fallen.

The next world empire (the sixth) **"is"** current to John's time.

In John's day that could only be the Roman Empire by which he was being persecuted and exiled to the island of Patmos.

The seventh world empire, as of John's time, has **"not yet come"** implying that it is in the process of coming. The question is: Could it be the **revived** Roman Empire mentioned in verse 8 that *was, is not, and yet is?*

The Roman Empire was (in Jesus' days), **is not** (for many centuries, including now), **and yet is** (poised to rise again in the great tribulation) headed up by the antichrist.

Rev.17: 11 tells us that there is an eighth world empire. The eighth could be Mystery Babylon, possibly headquartered in Europe and headed up by the antichrist, and still be part of the seventh; the seventh empire being the revived Roman Empire which will probably be headquartered in Europe.

Rev. 17: 12, 13 Ten independent rulers, who have been loyal to the antichrist, will meet with him briefly (one hour). They will unite with one mind, joining forces, and giving their power and strength to the beast. Antichrist will then give them their marching orders. **Destroy Israel !**

Although the Roman Empire was considered a world empire it was limited primarily to Europe. The scope and range of Mystery Babylon will be worldwide.

It would seem that the three kings who had been uprooted by the antichrist must have been replaced by three kings who will be more compliant to him because the number of kings is back up from 7 to 10.

Rev. 17:14 This reconstituted coalition of 10 kings will cross the dried up Euphrates River moving westward to fight the final battle of Armageddon designed to drive Israel into the Mediterranean Sea. Excluded from the rapture by God's design; Israel must still be on earth for this attack on their homeland to happen.

This could be Satan's last chance to destroy the Jews and to prevent one of God's most important prophecies. (Ezekiel 37: 27, 28) *My tabernacle also shall be with them: yea, "I will be their God and they shall be my people. And the heathen shall know that I the Lord do sanctify Israel, when my sanctuary shall be in the midst of them for evermore."*

If Satan could prove God a liar by destroying the Jewish nation then God could **not** legally condemn him to the lake of fire where he will be tormented day and night forever and ever *(Rev.20: 10.)* The lake of fire is Satan's worst fear.

The harlot is sitting on the backs of and at the expense of the various nations of the world. The antichrist has been arrogant and self serving, and yet expecting their full cooperation at the battle of Armageddon.

Verse 16 says the 10 horns (The 10 kingdoms of the coalition) will hate the harlot. They will make her desolate and burn her with fire. They will turn against Babylon. Why do they turn against Babylon? I don't know. Perhaps she was living in too much luxury at their expense.

I only know that *verse 17* tells us God has put in the hearts of these 10 kings to fulfill **His will**. This is not the battle of Armageddon but the destruction of

Mystery Babylon by the 10 king coalition. Armageddon is yet to come because the 10 king coalition also hates Israel, and is bent on their destruction.

But the effects of the 7th bowl judgment, which includes a great worldwide earthquake, will be the destruction of "Babylon" the headquarter city of this wicked world system.

In chapter 18 we will find that the destruction of Babylon was probably the result of a nuclear blast.

REVELATION   Chapter 18 A   The Fall of Babylon
Last 3 ½ years   *The Wrath of God*

The last three verses of *Ch.17* imply that Babylon may have been destroyed by disgruntled allied forces. *Rev.17: 16, 17* sounds as if the 10 kingdoms coalition has turned on Babylon, "for God has put in their heart to fulfill His will."

God will use the 10 king coalition by which Babylon is supported to destroy her, possibly with a nuclear bomb. It is the most probable way that a large metropolis could be destroyed and burned in one hour.

Rev.18: 9, 10: Standing afar off for fear of her torment, (Radiation fallout) the kings of the earth shall say, Alas, alas, that great city Babylon, that mighty city! For in one hour is thy judgment come.

Rev.18: 4 After Babylon is lying in ruin John hears a voice from heaven saying "Come out of her **my people;** be not partakers of her sin and receive not her plagues.

"Come out of her" does not refer to the city of Babylon because at that time it will be in total ruin, but rather to her system of sin and degradation.

The words, **"my people"** would imply that this voice is the voice of God Himself and these words are directed to God's ***chosen*** people, **Israel,** who are still present on earth.

The words **"my people"** are not referring to Gentile believers because God has gotten them out of harms way via the rapture before His undiluted wrath began.

By God's design, the **unbelieving** Jews were **not** included in the rapture, so there will be a large percent of Jewish people still on earth during the great tribulation.

Rev. 18: 5-7 The sins of this great city Babylon have reached unto heaven and God has remembered every last one of them.

Obadiah 1:15 says "For the day of the Lord is near upon all the heathen: as thou hast done, it shall be done unto thee: thy reward shall return upon thine own head."

Rewarding Babylon double according to her works is not unjust punishment on God's part. She was not only drunk with the blood of the saints and martyrs but due to her lack of remorse and her arrogant life style, God has doubled her reward.

Rev. 18: 8-10 Babylon's punishment will be quick. One day when she thinks she is safe and secure, death, morning, famine and fire will consume her.

REVELATION Chapter 18 B Lamentations for Babylon
Last 3 ½ years *The Wrath of God*

Rev. 18: 9, 10 The **kings of the earth** who engaged in immorality with her are now lamenting her loss. From afar off they can see the devastating judgment of God that took place in one hour. Most likely they keep their distance to avoid radiation fallout from a nuclear blast.

Obviously, they had a strong emotional attachment to this metropolitan harlot. Keep in mind that the harlot is **not** a literal woman; it will be a beautiful but evil metropolitan city, and a corrupt world system that influences the morals of the entire world.

It will probably be located somewhere in the former Roman Empire and it will be the headquarter city of the antichrist.

Rev. 18:13, 14 The merchants have no market for their merchandise such as gold, silver, precious stones, ivory, grains, cattle, fruits, **slaves, and the souls of men.**

That these merchants trade in slavery and human trafficking shows how truly evil and heartless these people are.

Rev. 18:20 The voice from heaven calls for rejoicing over the destruction of Babylon. The voice tells all who are in heaven including the holy apostles and prophets to celebrate because God has avenged them.

Rev. 18:22, 23, 24 Never again will Babylon deceive the nations. Never again will she shed the blood of the martyrs and live in luxury without remorse. Never again will she blaspheme the name of the Lord; because in her was found the blood of prophets and saints and all who were slain upon the earth throughout the ages.

REVELATION Chapter 19 A Marriage Supper of the Lamb
Last 3 ½ years

Rev.19: 1, 2 John hears **one great voice** of many people in heaven praising God.

The harmony there is so perfect that they sound like one voice as they shout "Alleluia: Salvation, and glory, and honor, and power unto the Lord our God".

Did you know that, Hallelujah means "praise the Lord" in almost any language on earth?

Rev. 19: 4, 5, The 24 elders and the 4 beasts fell down and worshiped God who sat on the throne.

The 24 elders are likely to be the twelve sons of Jacob, whose name God changed to *Israel* back in the Old Testament. *Gen.35:10-12* The other 12 are likely to be the 12 New Testament disciples making a total of 24 elders.

The 4 beasts are likely to be Seraphim angels. These very powerful elite angels are fewer in number than the Cherubim angels and always seem to be in close proximity to the throne of God. *(Rev.4: 8, 9) (Isaiah 6: 2, 3)*

Rev. 19: 6 This great multitude in heaven is comprised of everyone whose name is written in the Lambs book of life; all who have accepted Jesus' invitation to the wedding feast. They were included in the first resurrection of the dead. The first resurrection is when these mortals will have received their immortal bodies.

Their souls have already been redeemed but their bodies are still waiting to be redeemed. That happens at the first resurrection of the dead; (which is the same as the rapture).

Rev. 19: 7 You can feel the excitement building as they say, "Let us be glad, and rejoice, and give honor to Him: for the marriage of the Lamb is come and His wife has made herself ready." Now we see what the excitement is all about; the marriage of the Lamb and His bride.

Rev. 19: 8 The bride is **given** the cleanest, whitest, finest linen that heaven can provide because it represents righteousness. Faithful believers are the bride of Christ. We do **not** come to Jesus with our own righteousness. It is given to us by Him.

Rev. 19: 9 Blessed indeed are they who are called to the marriage supper of the Lamb. They are not the guests but the bride of Christ. They have answered the call of God.

Let's take a closer look at the *"true church"*, the body of believers, the bride of Christ, as referenced in Eph.5:23-27.

Eph.5: 25 says Christ loved the church and gave himself for it. Believers are the church, the body of Christ. V: 23 says Jesus is the head of the church and the Savior of the body.

The ultimate goal of Jesus is to present, to *Himself*, this church that He paid such a heavy price for, and cared so much for by interceding for us through out the ages.

Eph.5: 27 says He sacrificed His own blood and now He wants to present to *Himself* this pure and holy church without spot, wrinkle, or blemish.

Folks, **we are** that church, **the bride** of Christ, and what is our part in preparing for this magnificent event?

Matt.22: 37-40 we must love the Lord with all our heart, soul, mind, and strength, and our neighbor as our selves. We must live holy, sanctified lives that are pleasing to God.

Rev. 19: 10 Overwhelmed at the thought of being called unto the marriage supper of the Lamb, John falls at the feet of the angel to worship him, but the angel says, "Do not do it, I am a fellow servant (a created being), worship God."

At this point we can assume that the wedding has taken place. From now on, wherever the groom is, the bride will also be.

REVELATION   Chapter 19 B   Battle of Armageddon
Last 3 ½ years   *The Wrath of God*

Rev. 19: 11-13 John sees heaven opened and a white horse whose rider is Jesus. The rider is called "Faithful and True and in righteousness He will judge and make war".

The rider on the white horse is described as having eyes as flames of fire, on his head were many crowns, his vesture dipped in blood, and His name is, The Word of God.

Jesus' vesture dipped in blood is from treading the wine press of the wrath of God (Rev.14:18-20). Those were the grapes of wrath spoken of in **Joel 3:13.**

This heavenly army which is the bride of Christ is about to leave heaven and come to earth with Jesus as their conquering leader to fight at the battle of Armageddon.

Rev. 19:14 His white horse represents a conquering leader. As He leads, the armies of heaven follow him on white horses wearing white linen (Representing righteousness).

One can almost hear them singing as they ride, **"Victory in Jesus my Savior forever."**

Rev. 19:15 Out of His mouth goes a sharp sword which is the word of God (Heb.4:12).

With the word of God He will smite the nations. He will defeat the coalition of 10 kings and their multi-national forces with the words of His mouth.

Rev. 19:16 King of Kings, Lord of Lords is written on the thigh of His vesture as He rides the white horse making it visible for anyone to see.

Is this the second return of Christ to the earth? **Yes,** but it has nothing to do with the rapture of believers when Jesus meets us in the air. *I Thess.4:16,17* At the rapture Jesus comes *for us*, but when He returns to earth to fight the battle of Armageddon He will come **with us,** or should I say **we** will come **with Him.**

Rev. 19: 17, 18 John saw an angel stand high in the sky, announcing to all the vultures and scavengers to gather themselves to a great feast. On the menu is the flesh of kings, captains, mighty men of the earth, and every level of society.

Rev. 19: 19 John sees the beast (antichrist) and the kings, and their armies. They are gathered together to make war against Him that sat on the white horse and against His army.

Apparently, Gog and Magog (An anti-Semitic territory north of Israel, **not** directly associated with the 10 king coalition) are also part of the attacking forces. This territory north of Israel is likely to be Russia.

Ezekiel 39:1-5 (Paraphrased) says, son of man prophesy against Gog. Thus says the Lord God; Behold, I am against you, *O Gog, I will turn you back and leave but a sixth part of you.* I will cause you to come up from the north parts, and bring you upon the mountains of Israel; you will fall on the mountains of Israel; you and the people who are with you. I will give your bodies to the ravenous birds and the scavengers of the field. (Referring to the battle of Armageddon)

Jesus is now coming as the Lion of Judah to fight the battle of Armageddon. His goal is to avenge His saints, overthrow the wicked world system, (the 10 kingdom coalition) and establish His Kingdom of righteousness on earth.

His primary weapon is a sharp sword that comes from His mouth. With this sword He will smite the nations, meaning that whatever He says, will bring about their destruction.

It is quite possible that whatever Jesus says to them will be so wise and so clever that it will literally cause them to turn on each other and fight each other to the death.

There are other examples of this happening in the Old Testament. When armies were about to fight against Israel, they end up fighting each other instead. Judges 7:22, 23

Ezekiel 38:18, 21 (paraphrased) "When Gog shall come against the land of Israel, says the Lord God that my fury shall come up in my face. I will call for a sword against him throughout all my mountains, saith the Lord God: every man's sword shall be against his brother."

As His bride, we will be there, but we may not have to fight at all. He has even made arrangements for the battle field to be cleaned up afterward by vultures and scavengers. *(Rev.19: 17, 18)*

Even with the help of the vultures and scavengers, it will still take Israel seven months to bury the dead according to *Ezekiel 39: 4, 9-12*

Rev. 19:20 Two of the earliest casualties of this war are the beast (antichrist) and the false prophet who performed miracles to deceive those who received the mark of the beast or worshipped his image. *(Rev.13: 11-14)*

Both of them (antichrist and false prophet) were cast alive into the lake of fire that was **created for the devil and his angels.** (Matt.25: 41) The lake of fire was not originally created for people. It was created for the devil and his angels; nevertheless, those who reject Jesus Christ and identify themselves with the devil and his angels will go there.

Rev.20:10 says, they shall be tormented day and night for ever and ever. Can you imagine what that would be like? No relief, no rest, no mercy, no hope, nothing but pain and regret for all eternity.

Rev. 19:21 The remnant of the multi-national coalition who did not kill each other, were slain with the sword of Him that sat upon the white horse. (Jesus finished them off).

It was they who conspired with the antichrist to shed the blood of the saints and martyrs, so we don't need to feel sorry for these people.

They refused a decent burial for the two witnesses in Ch.11, and gloated over their deaths. Now the fowls of the air will gorge themselves on the flesh of these arrogant fools.

After the battle of Armageddon there will still be many people on earth who have somehow survived the great tribulation. They did not willingly take the mark of the beast, they did not participate in the battle at Armageddon, nor have they accepted Jesus Christ as their personal Savior. They still have a chance to be saved as Jesus begins to set up His kingdom on earth; the millennial reign of Christ.

REVELATION Chapter 20 A
The millennial reign of Christ
Satan Arrested and Imprisoned 1000 years

Rev.19: 20 said the antichrist and the false prophet were both cast alive into the lake of fire burning with brimstone, but what about Satan, the third member of the unholy trinity. What will happen to him?

Rev. 20: 1, 2 John sees an angel (*officer*) descend from heaven (*the justice center*) with the key (*jailer's key*) to the bottomless pit (*jail*) and with a chain (*hand cuffs*) in his hand.

He laid hold of (*arrested*) the dragon, *also known as,* the serpent, *also known as,* the Devil, *a.k.a.* Satan, (*the criminal*) and bound him (*cuffed him*) and cast him (*stuffed him*) into the bottomless pit (*the slammer*) for 1000 years.

Rev. 20: 3 This lawless, vicious, threat to society is bound. The King James Version says he's **"shut up"** and sealed. (Satan is shut up and sealed shut for 1000 years). The reason he is locked up and sealed is so he can not deceive the nations for 1000 years.

After Satan's defeat in the war that occurred in heaven against Michael and his angels, Satan lost free access to heaven and was then cast down to earth. *(12: 7-12)*

He lost a lot of his rank and authority. He later looses the battle at Armageddon. Then he looses his ability to move about and to deceive the nations. Satan is a loser.

However, after the 1000 years are fulfilled, (after he serves his jail time), Satan must be released for a short time. We will learn more about that later.

Jesus is about to set up His Kingdom on earth called the millennial reign of Christ. During that 1000 years Satan will be jailed in the bottomless pit. I don't know for sure if the bottomless pit is Hades, but if it is then Satan will be locked up in his own jail.

Most people accept that a "glorified Jesus" will return physically to earth at His second coming to fight and win the battle of Armageddon. Then He will establish an earthly Kingdom where He will reign from the throne of David for 1000 years. Many of the Old Testament promises to Israel will be fulfilled at that time of peace.

Rev. 20: 4, 5 John sees in heaven the souls of martyrs who are given a special status for their proven faithfulness, as they refused to accept the mark of the beast. The rest of the dead (the lost) lived not until the 1000 years were finished. (After the millennium)

Lost people in graves will stay there another 1000 years before they are judged. The first resurrection (for believers) is before the 1000 years and the second resurrection (for unbelievers) is after the 1000 year Reign of Christ. It's called "The Great White Throne Judgment."

Rev. 20:6 says: Blessed and holy is he that hath part in the first resurrection: on such the second death (The lake of fire) hath no power, but they shall be priests of God, and of Christ, and shall reign with Him a thousand years."

Rev. 20:6 Blessed and holy is the believer who has part in the **first resurrection, but when does it happen in relation to the rapture of believers?** How far apart is the rapture and the first resurrection of believers?

True Christians differ on their views of: Pre, Mid, and Post tribulation rapture. Regardless of which view we adopt, how can we justify a rapture of believers that occurs just prior to the first resurrection of believers?

Since the 7 years of tribulation (Including the rapture of the dead in Christ) occurs just before the millennium and the first resurrection of the faithful also occurs just before the millennium that would put the rapture and the first resurrections almost back to back. What would be the point of that?

However, it would possibly make sense if the rapture of believers and the first resurrection of believers *are the same thing.* Rev. 20: verse 6 might be referring to the rapture when it says ….

"Blessed and holy is he that has part in the **first resurrection (the rapture)**: on such the second death has no power (no condemnation) but they shall be priests of God and of Christ and shall reign with Him (on earth) 1000 years." *Rev.20: 6*

There are three huge groups that will continue to exist on earth during the 1000 year reign of Christ. **1.** Jesus and His glorified bride which is the body of Christ. **2.** The faithful 144,000 Jewish believers. **3.** Unsaved Tribulation survivors who did not accept the mark of the beast. *Isaiah 2:4* says something interesting about the tribulation survivors who did not take the mark of the beast.

Isaiah 2:4 referring to Jesus says: **He shall judge among the nations, and shall rebuke many people: and they shall beat their swords into plowshares, and their spears into pruning hooks: nation shall not lift up sword against nation; neither shall they learn war any more.** Jesus neither praises nor condemns them, but He rebukes them (He instructs them) and they listen.

Who are these former warriors? They are **unsaved** tribulation survivors who did not take the mark of the beast. Many of them actively opposed the antichrist. When Jesus rebukes them they will give up their weapons and live in peace with their fellow man. These are decent people who have not yet been led to Jesus.

Perhaps this is when Jesus will sit upon His millennial throne and gather before Him all of the nations of the world to separate the sheep from the goats. The sheep on His right hand could be those who opposed the antichrist and aided the people of God during the first 3 ½ years of tribulation even though they didn't know they were serving Jesus. They will be spared.

The goats on His left hand could be those tribulation survivors who willingly received the mark of the beast. They will be eliminated.

Matt. 25: 31-46   Jesus Separates the Sheep from the Goats

Matt. 25: 31 When the Son of man shall come in His glory, and the holy angels with Him, then shall He sit upon the throne of His glory.

When does this happen? It happens right after He returns to earth to fight and win the battle of Armageddon. Then He will begin to reign on earth for 1000 years as He sits on the throne of His glory.

Matt. 25: 32 and before Him shall be gathered all nations: and He shall separate them one from another, as a shepherd divides his sheep from his goats.

This judgment has nothing to do with a resurrection from the dead. The angels will gather all nations to King Jesus for the purpose of sorting and separating tribulation survivors as to who will be allowed to enter into the earthly Kingdom of Jesus Christ and who will be executed and sent to Hades.

Matt. 25: 33-36 He shall sit the sheep on His right hand but the goats on His left. Then shall the King say unto the sheep on His right hand. Come ye blessed of my Father, inherit the kingdom prepared for you from the foundation of the world. For I was an hungered, and ye gave me meat: I was thirsty, and ye gave me drink: I was a stranger, and ye took me in: Naked and ye clothed me: I was sick, and ye visited me: I was in prison, and ye came unto me.

Matt. 25: 37-39 Then shall the righteous answer (paraphrased) Lord, when did we do all those things for you?

They are called righteous for two reasons; because of their position at the right hand of Jesus and second because they did the right thing by opposing the antichrist and helping God's people.

The sheep on His right could be those who opposed the antichrist and aided the people of God during the first 3 ½ years of the tribulation even though they were **not** saved and didn't know they were serving Jesus. They could be predestinated from the foundation of the world to be saved during the millennial reign of Christ.

Matt. 25: 40 and the King shall answer and say unto them, Verily I say unto you, insomuch as ye have done it unto one of the least of these my brothers, ye have done it unto me. They were **not saved** by their good works but they were **spared** because their good works identified whose side they were on; the side of righteousness.

Remember Joshua chapter 2: when Joshua sent the two spies to Jericho where they were hidden and protected by Rahab the pagan prostitute because she had heard that their God had miraculously delivered the Israelites from the bondage of Egypt. She was not part of the people of God and yet she and her family were **spared** from destruction and later included into the family of God.

Hebrews 11:31 By faith the harlot Rahab perished **not** with them that believed **not**, when she had received the spies with peace.

Rahab was **not** saved by her good works but she was **spared** from condemnation because of her faith in the only true God, she rejected pagan worship and aided the people of God. Her good works identified whose side she was on; ***the side of righteousness.*** After the tribulation of her time was over she was formally included into the family of God by faith.

Matt. 25: 41-43 then shall He say unto them on the left hand. Depart from me you cursed, into everlasting fire, prepared for the devil and his angels: for I was an hungered and ye gave me no meat; I was thirsty, and ye gave me no drink: I was a stranger and ye took me not in: naked and ye clothed me not: sick, and in prison and ye visited me not.

Matt. 25: 44 Then shall they also answer Him saying (paraphrased) Lord, when did we **not** minister to your needs?

Matt. 25: 45 Then shall He answer them, saying, verily , I say unto you, insomuch as ye did it **not** unto one of the least of these, ye did it **not** unto me. They obviously had an opportunity to help God's people during their time of affliction but they didn't do it. So, whether they took the mark or not they identified themselves with the devil and his angels.

Matt. 25: 46 Jesus says, "These shall go away into everlasting punishment: but the righteous into life eternal."

Most likely the angels will execute those on the left. They will die in their sins and go to Hades.

The righteous (those who did the right thing) will be *spared* and welcomed into the millennial Kingdom of Jesus Christ where they will hopefully be led to a personal relationship with Jesus.

Some solid believers insist that some people will be saved during the second 3 ½ years of the tribulation; which is the wrath of God. If that were true those babes in Christ would be un-scripturally subjected to the undiluted wrath of God. *I Thess. 5: 9*

Although there is evidence that the 144,000 Jews will be present and protected from the wrath of God, I see no evidence that these Gentiles will be present or protected. Although the Holy Spirit will probably be present to convict people of their sins; the Holy Spirit is more likely to be **on** them than **in** them.

Keep in mind that just before God's wrath begins the gospel will be preach around the world in three different ways. **First:** God's great commission to the church. *Mark 16:15.* **Second:** The two powerful witnesses who preach from the streets of Jerusalem in *Rev. 11: 3* and **Third:** an angel will fly around the world preaching the everlasting gospel to every nation. *Rev. 14: 6.* To reject all of this, people would have to close the door of their heart very deliberately.

When God closed the door on Noah's ark, it was closed and sealed. Aren't you glad He didn't leave it open just a crack so the late comers could slip in after the rains began?

However, some tribulation survivors will have another chance to be saved during the millennial reign of Christ. They may be counted as sheep and allowed to live in the Kingdom of Jesus Christ where they will hopefully be led to a personal relationship with Jesus. God is not willing that any should perish. What a gracious Savior He is!

What is the purpose of the 1000 year millennium?

When Christ Jesus reigns on earth with a scepter of righteousness it will be a time of love, peace, and safety for all of His chosen and faithful people because Satan is bound.

Isaiah 11:6-9 (Paraphrased) The wolf shall dwell with the lamb, and the leopard shall lie down with the kid; and the calf and the young lion together; and a little child shall lead them. The cow and the bear shall feed; their young ones shall lie down together: and the lion shall eat straw like the ox. The sucking child shall play on the hole of the Asp. They shall not hurt or destroy in all my holy mountain: the earth shall be full of the knowledge of the Lord, as the waters cover the sea.

Notice that the lion will eat straw like the ox. The lion will no longer be carnivorous. Wild animals will be tamed. The knowledge and spirit of the Lord will be prevalent.

Believers will be assigned millennial areas of authority. They will rule and represent King Jesus in specific locations throughout the world. Our inheritance, rewards, and reign are based on our present earthly faithfulness, works, service, and perseverance for Christ.

Rev. 5: 9-10 The **redeemed** of the Lord will be kings and priests who will reign on earth with Christ for 1000 years.

Over whom will they rule and reign? There will be many people who have somehow made it through the great tribulation without choosing to take the mark of the beast. They were not involved in the battle of Armageddon, **nor** have they received Jesus Christ in their lifetime. Here are more people who still have a chance to be saved.

Satan is bound and is not present to deceive them. If they show any sign of rebellion against the King, immediate punitive action will be taken against them. They will be killed as Christ will rule with a rod of iron. (Rev.19:15)

The purpose of the millennium might be for God to prove that man's heart is evil by his Adamic nature. Because we are all descendants of Adam, man has a propensity to sin with or without the influence of Satan. They can not say, "The devil made me do it."

During this 1000 year time of peace when Satan is bound, there will probably be a population explosion on this earth. These unsaved tribulation survivors who are still on earth need to be indoctrinated into the Christian faith; but by whom?

Rev. 20: 6 The redeemed priests of God are to indoctrinate these people into the Christian faith during the 1000 year reign of Christ. The redeemed priests of God are us. We will attempt to lead these tribulation survivors (The sheep) to King Jesus.

This might be the gleaning of the four corners of the earth after the main harvest known as the first resurrection (or rapture) has been accomplished.

Most people who say the prayer that Jesus taught in Matt.6: 9-13 don't realize that when they say "Thy kingdom come, thy will be done, on earth as it is in heaven" could actually be referring to "the millennial reign of Christ," as well as this present age of grace.

During the 1000 year millennial reign of Christ on earth. There are three major groups that will be there. The first group: Jesus and His bride (the body of Christ) will reign with immortal bodies as priests of God.

Second: The 144,000 faithful Jewish believers will have mortal bodies.

The third group is the tribulation survivors who did not take the mark of the beast. They will be there in mortal bodies and they will reproduce. The tribulation survivors were the sheep who were on His right hand, while the goats on His left hand were eliminated.

How these mortal beings will interact with the immortal beings is a mystery but it will probably be like it was when Jesus interacted with the two disciples on the road to Emmaus, or with His disciples in the upper room after His resurrection. Luke 24:13-43

During that 1000 years Satan will be bound and there will be a population explosion on this earth. People who die during those 1000 years will either go to heaven or hell just as they do now. They will be resurrected and judged at the Great White Throne judgment. *John 5: 28, 29*

John 5: 28, 29 Marvel not at this: for the hour is coming, in the which all that are in the graves shall hear His voice, and shall come forth; they that have done good, unto the resurrection of life; and they that have done evil, unto the resurrection of damnation.

Notice that the Great White Throne, unlike the first resurrection, is the only judgment in which both the good and the evil are resurrected at the same time. The good are tribulation survivors saved during the millennial reign of Christ.

The evil are all those of every generation who's names are not written in the Lamb's book of life due to unbelief.

REVELATION   Chapter 20 B   Great White Throne Judgment
The Final Judgment

Rev.20: 7 After the thousand years are completed, Satan must be released from prison (the bottomless pit). He will return to his same activities as before to deceive the nations in the four quarters of the earth (the entire world).

So far Satan has succeeded in deceiving the Jewish people for 2000 years as they still do **not** accept Jesus as their Messiah, but during the great tribulation they will awaken from their spiritual slumber *(Rom.11: 7, 8)* and know that Jesus is their true Messiah. When Satan can no longer deceive the Jewish people, he will try to destroy them.

At the beginning of the 7 years of tribulation the antichrist made a peace treaty between the Jews and the Arabs. When Israel is finished building their temple in Jerusalem, after 3 ½ years the antichrist will break the treaty and try to destroy them.

God protected and nurtured them the last 3 ½ years of the great tribulation. Then the antichrist tried to drive them into the Mediterranean Sea at Armageddon and failed. Now after 1000 years of peace Satan is released and has one last chance to destroy Israel.

Rev. 20: 8 Satan is released and again he goes out to deceive the nations of the world. He will point out to the nations the difference between what they have **compared** to what Israel and Jerusalem have. Jerusalem will be the capital city of the world during the millennial reign of Christ.

The earthly Kingdom and Throne of Jesus Christ will be lavish and glorious; well beyond that of Solomon's kingdom temple. This will be common knowledge throughout the world.

Satan will introduce to the world a concept that had never really crossed their minds while he was bound. Satan will instill *envy* and *jealousy* into the nations and tempt them to *"spread the wealth"*.

Satan will gather innumerable multi-national forces including Gog and

Magog, (an anti-Semitic territory north of Israel **not** directly associated with the 10 kingdom coalition. This territory north of Israel is probably Russia.) These forces combine to surround, destroy, and plunder Israel.

The original 10 kingdom coalition will not be involved in this battle because they were destroyed at the battle of Armageddon.

Ezekiel 39:1-4 Tells us that **a sixth part** of Gog and Magog were spared at the battle of Armageddon prior to the 1000 year millennial reign of Christ. That sixth part, or rather their descendants, will live to fight again in this final battle.

Up till this time the faith and commitment of the tribulation survivors and their descendants had not been tested. They were easily led to the Lord while Satan was bound, but then many of them will fall for Satan's deception and prove that their commitment was not real. They will agree to help plunder Israel. Tribulation survivors are the only possible source of these warriors.

Rev. 20: 9 When they surround the beloved City of God (Jerusalem), fire will come down out of heaven and devour them.

Rev. 20:10 At that time the devil is cast into the lake of fire where the beast and the false prophet are, and shall be tormented day and night forever and ever. At that time Satan's worst fear will become his reality.

They will not cease to exist. Their annihilation would be an act of mercy, but they will receive no mercy. There is no need of a formal trial for the unholy trinity. They were in direct opposition to God on every front.

Rev. 20: 11 John sees a ***great white throne*** and Him that sat on the throne. The one seated on the throne is Jesus because *John 5:22* tells us that the Father has entrusted all judgment to the Son.

John sees something spectacular; the earth and sky fled from the presence of Him that sat on the throne. This could mean that Sovereign God, at this time will destroy the universe that He created including the earth itself which He calls "the first heaven and the first earth." *Rev.21: 1*

Rev. 21: 1 says: And I saw a New Heaven and a New Earth: for the first heaven and the first earth were passed away; and there was no sea.

Rev. 20:12 John sees the resurrected dead stand before the throne of God and the books (plural) were opened. The book of life was also opened. The dead were judged out of those books according to their works. (This is the second and final resurrection).

The first earth will pass away but verse 13 indicates that God will remove all the deceased for judgment before that happens.

Rev.20: 5, 6 these are "the rest of the dead"; those who missed the first resurrection because of unbelief. They are judged out of the books (plural) containing their works. (Eph.2: 8-9) says they can not be saved by their good works. These books will contain every sin, every careless word, every secret thought or deed they have ever committed.

The great white throne judgment is for people who did **not** have part in the first resurrection. This second resurrection is primarily for all the lost of every generation.

However, there is another book that will be opened at the Great White Throne judgment. It is the book of life.

By the grace of God, many who survived the great tribulation, and their descendants, will be saved during the 1000 year reign of Christ. These people are primarily Gentiles who survived the great tribulation without taking the mark of the beast. Many of them will be led to the Lord by saints who reign as priests of God in the millennium. *Rev.20: 6*

Rev. 20: 6 "Blessed and holy is he that has part in the first resurrection: on such the second death has no power, (no condemnation) but they shall be priests of God and of Christ, and shall reign with Him for one thousand years." These priests will lead many of the tribulation survivors to King Jesus.

Rev. 20:13 The Sea gave up its' dead, **death and hell** gave up its dead, and they too were judged according to their works. **Ephesians 2: 8, 9** tells us they **can not** be saved by their good works. They can only be saved by faith in the finished work of Jesus Christ.

Rev. 20:14, 15 tells us *"death and hell"* were cast into the lake of fire, **and**

whosoever's name was not written in the book of life was cast into the lake of fire *which is the second death.* That could be anyone who rejects Jesus Christ as their personal Savior. We need to be absolutely certain that our name is written in the Lamb's book of life. John 3: 3 says: Except a man be "born again," he cannot see the kingdom of God. So it's very important that we know...... **How to be a Born Again Christian.**

How to be a Born Again Christian

1. **Confession:** Agree with God that you are a sinner.
   We are sinners, not because we sin, but because we have a sinful nature. We did not become sinners by sinning. We were born with the propensity to sin because of our selfish nature.

2. **Repentance:** Being sincerely sorry for every sin you have ever committed. We should love what God loves, and hate what God hates. We should hate sin because God hates sin, but He does not hate sinners.

3. **Believe:** that Jesus Christ is the sinless Son of God and that the innocent blood He shed on the cross was sufficient for the forgiveness of your sins. Faith is taking God at His word [the bible].

4. **Invite** Jesus Christ, to come into your heart and be the Lord of your life. Jesus said, "I stand at the door [of your heart] and knock. If any man invites me in I will come in." Rev. 3:20
   Acts 2:21 says whosoever shall call on the name of the Lord shall be saved.

5. **Ask** God to fill you with the Holy Spirit and help you understand His word [the bible] and His will for your life. Teaching and understanding **is** a function of the Holy Spirit, the third person of the trinity.

6. **Thank, Praise, and Serve** God for giving you the gift of eternal life. Then we must grow into spiritual maturity. This takes time, experience, and a grateful heart. Remember that your second birth is just as real and just as important as your first birth.

REVELATION   Chapter 21 A
The New Heaven, New Earth, and New Jerusalem

Rev. 21: 1 John sees a New Heaven and a New Earth, for the first heaven and earth had passed away. The question is: Why did they pass away and how did they pass away?

Why this present earth must pass away is answered best in **Rom. 8:21, 22:** The creature itself also shall be delivered from the bondage of corruption into the glorious liberty of the children of God. For we know that the whole creation groaneth and travaileth in pain together until now.

This sin laden world must be delivered from the bondage of corruption, and until it is, it will groan and travail in suffering and degradation. Some think this earth will be restored and continue on forever but according to Rev.21:5 God will make all things new.

But first, II Peter 3:10-13 tells us "the heavens shall pass away with a great noise, and the elements shall melt with fervent heat. The earth also and the works that are therein shall be burned up."

Isaiah 65:17 says "Behold, I create a new heaven and a new earth: and the **former** shall not be remembered, nor come into mind."

This might be a good thing because **if** we did remember things about this earth we might have a lot of sadness and regrets to deal with. Loved ones who were spiritually lost and bound for hell may not ever be remembered. There will be no sorrow in the new heaven.

By the end of Chapter 20 of Revelation we see all those who would do evil, both human and angelic, have been cast into the lake of fire. Evil is gone forever.

Isaiah 65:17, 18 (paraphrased) tells us **not** to be sad about this, but to rejoice in the **creation** of a new heaven, a new earth, and a New Jerusalem, inhabited by those who share the joy of knowing their Lord and Savior.

Rev. 21: 2 John sees the New Jerusalem coming down from God out of heaven, prepared as a bride adorned for her husband. (It will be breathtakingly beautiful) Where does the New Jerusalem land? It lands on the New Earth.

Rev. 21: 3 At that time God's most important prophecy to His chosen people will be fulfilled. Ezekiel 37: 27, 28 *My tabernacle also shall be with them: yea, I will be their God, and they shall be my people. And the heathen shall know that I the Lord do sanctify Israel, when my sanctuary shall be in the midst of them for evermore.*

Rev. 21: 4 We may not know much about what will be in the New Jerusalem, but we can know what will not be there: **no more** tears, death, sorrow, pain, sickness, crying, headaches, heartaches, or any such thing.

Rev. 21: 5, 6 Then He said to John, "Write for these words are true and faithful." **"It is done".**

What is done? God's justice has been served and His people have been avenged. Evil in every form has been crushed and punished.

Now it is time for rewards. Jesus is the author and finisher of our faith, but our faith is not finished until His faithful saints have been glorified and rewarded. The Lord says, "I will give unto him that is athirst of the fountain of the water of life freely."

Rev. 21: 7 God declares, "Overcomers shall inherit **all** things; I will be his God and he shall be my son." The children of God are joint heirs with Jesus. Rom. 8:17

Rev. 21: 9, 10 One of the 7 powerful angels who poured out the bowls says to John, "Come and I will show you the bride, the Lamb's wife". He carried John away in the spirit to a great high mountain, and showed him a great city, the Holy Jerusalem.

Rev. 21:11 The source of the splendor and brilliance of this city is the glory of God.

John 14:3 Jesus said "I go to prepare a place for you, (My promised bride) I will come again, and receive you unto myself; that where I am, there you may be also."

This implies that our eternal home is being prepared every day as Jesus observes our every thought, word, and deed. It is uniquely designed for His eternal "soul mate". It perfectly reflects every need, desire, and passion His bride will ever experience. The New Jerusalem, as shown to John by the angel, literally represents the bride of Christ.

Rev. 21:12, 13 The city is surrounded by a wall on each of four sides. On each wall there were 3 gates and on those 12 gates are the names of the 12 tribes of the children of Israel. There is an angel stationed at each of the 12 gates.

Unlike the cherubim who guarded against access to the tree of life after the fall of Adam and Eve in the Garden of Eden; *Gen.3:24* these angels are "honor guards" implying that it is a privilege to enter the dwelling place of God. (They are like greeters). We will have full access to the tree of life.

Rev. 21:14 "The wall of the city had **twelve foundations**, and in them the names of the twelve apostles of the Lamb."

Forevermore, the 12 gates will honor the 12 tribes of Old Testament Israel, and the 12 foundations will forever honor the New Testament apostles of the church of Christ. Together they honor the 24 elders.

REVELATION   Chapter 21 B   *"NEW JERUSALEM"*
The City that is Built Four Square

Rev.21:15,16 The angel had a golden reed to measure the holy city, the gates, and the walls.

New Jerusalem measured four square, the length, breadth, and height of it being equal.

It measured twelve thousand furlongs which would be about 1400 miles in each direction, and then 1400 miles high.

The length, breadth, and height of the New Jerusalem are equal. What geometric figure does that remind you of ?

There are three geometric figures that can have the same length, breadth, and height.

They are a sphere, a cube, and a four sided pyramid. The question is: How can we know which one applies to the New Jerusalem in this case?

The answer could be in verse 16; **the city lays "four square."** This means that, as a geometric figure it can only be squared (with a right angle carpenters square) in four different ways. The sphere is eliminated because it cannot be squared at all.

A **cube** lays 12 square because it can be squared 12 different ways, but a four sided **pyramid** can only be squared in four different ways. It can only be squared on each of the four corners at the base of the pyramid.

The four sided pyramid is therefore the only true 4 square geometric figure that exists.

If the New Jerusalem is shaped like a four sided pyramid, it is truly *"The city that is built four square."* The pyramid is also the most stable and secure geometric figure in that it is the most difficult to topple.

An example of a four sided pyramid can be seen on the back of a one dollar bill and the great pyramids of Egypt are also 4 sided pyramids.

Rev. 21:17-20 Without getting into the details, it suffices to say that this city is magnificent beyond our wildest imagination. The wall around the city is **not** to keep evil out, because there is no more evil, but rather to define the city's borders.

Rev. 21:21 The 12 gates were made of one pearl each and the streets were made of purest gold as it were transparent glass. (Both defy human understanding)

Rev. 21:22 There is no temple in the New Jerusalem. Why is there no temple in the New Jerusalem?

In the Old Testament the temple was a place of divine provision for sinful man. Through blood sacrifices and offerings, sinful man could come into the presence of God. There was a veil separating them and only the high priest could enter once a year. Heb.9: 6, 7

Heb. 9:11, 12 (paraphrased) but Jesus, the Lamb of God and our high priest, entered the holy place, for our redemption and offered **not** the blood of goats and calves but His body and His blood **once for all**. In John 2:19-21 Jesus spoke of His body as being the temple of sacrifice. Therefore, since there will be no sin in heaven a temple of sacrifice will no longer be necessary.

Rev. 21:23 The city had no need of the sun or moon, for the glory of God, and of the Lamb did lighten it. There is a parallel passage in *Isaiah 60:19*.

Isaiah 60:19 The sun shall be no more thy light by day; neither for brightness shall the moon give light unto thee: but the Lord shall be unto thee an everlasting light, and thy God, thy glory.

John 8:12 Jesus is the light of the world. **That light** came into the world, and men loved darkness rather than light because their sins were evil. *(John 3:19)*

Rev. 21:25, 26 The gates of the eternal city will never be shut. There is no night there and no need of physical security.

Rev. 21:27 There will be no evil or corruption of any kind entering this city because only righteous people whose names are written in the Lambs book of life will live there. They were once darkened by sin, but now they walk in the light of the Lord. *Eph. 5: 8*

Since people die at different ages on earth but live forever in heaven, you might wonder what age we are likely to be in heaven. Did you ever wonder about that? What ever age it is, it will probably never change. There will be no aging process there.

Mark 16:1-6 verses 5 and 6 say: entering into the sepulcher (Tomb) they saw *a young man* sitting on the right side clothed in white garment: and they were affrighted. He saith unto them "be not affrighted: you seek Jesus of Nazareth which was crucified: He is risen: He is not here.

Most likely *the young man* at the tomb was an angel (In his prime). Luke 20:36 says, neither can they die anymore for they are equal to the angels: and are the children of God: being the children of the resurrection. This could imply that our new glorified bodies *might forever be young adults in our prime* like the angels.

Nevertheless, there will always be a difference between the angels, and the saints of God who have been redeemed, because angels can not be redeemed once they have fallen.

REVELATION   Chapter 22 A   The River and Tree of Life

Rev.22: 1 The angel shows John a pure river of water of life, clear as crystal, flowing out of the throne of God and of the Lamb.

Present day believers think of the Holy Spirit of God as a river of life flowing out from the throne of God. Jesus was speaking of the Holy Spirit when He offered living water to the woman at the well. *John 4:10-14;* and this is a visible river of life flowing from the throne that John can actually see.

On either side of the bank of the river, and in the midst of it, was the tree of life which yielded 12 manners of fruit, apparently a different fruit for each month of the year. Yes, there will be months and years in heaven. There will be recorded time. When we've been there 10,000 years we will know it and celebrate it.

This life giving water flows from the throne of God; it goes wherever God chooses as it flows out to the various nations on the new earth. Yes there will be nations and a system of government on the new earth.

Rev. 21: verse one implies "there are no oceans, or large seas on the new earth," but there will be **no** shortage of water ways bringing living water to all of the inhabitants of the new earth. If this present earth will be restored and continue on forever, as some people say, then where would the massive oceans and seas of this world go?

With no oceans or seas much more of the new earth will be inhabitable. There will be plenty of room for everyone including the billions of people who died prematurely as babies. It is likely that there will be rivers, streams, ponds and lakes but no bodies of water large enough to constitute a sea. *Rev. 21: 1*

Present day believers regularly bring their tithes and offerings to the house of the Lord and receive intangible blessings in return. Here, we do this to offset operating expenses, and to facilitate future church growth. On the new earth, in the new heaven, we will bring offerings to increase the glory and honor of the government of our Lord and King.

Isaiah 9: 7 says, *of the increase of His government and peace there shall be no end,* upon the throne of David, and upon His Kingdom, to order it, and to establish it with judgment and with justice from henceforth *even forever.* The zeal of the Lord of hosts will perform this.

This seems to say that whatever His eternal Kingdom is; unlike His 1000 year earthly Kingdom, there will be no end to the increase of it. The heavenly Kingdom of Jesus Christ will forever continue to *increase* and *expand*. In heaven no one will ever ask "Is this all there is; have I seen it all?"

John 14:3 Jesus said "I go to prepare a place for you, (My bride) I will come again, and receive you unto myself; that where I am, there ye may be also.

As the bride of Jesus we will be His helpmate. We will be intimately involved in everything that happens in the New Heaven. Our common goal will be to increase the glory, honor, comfort, and enjoyment of His Kingdom; which is our eternal home.

There will **not** be a monetary system on the new earth but Jesus did say that we should store up for our selves treasures in heaven where moth and rust do not destroy, and where thieves do not break in and steal. *Matt.6:20*

Many of the treasures in heaven will be there because of the thoughtful prayers, precious words of wisdom, and sacrificial deeds of kindness that were done on this earth in secret. The Father who sees what is done in secret will openly reward His faithful saints.

Jesus' death on the tree at Calvary made it possible for believers to have access to the tree of life found in the New Jerusalem.

It's **not** likely that there is any waste on the new earth. It could be that when we drink of the water of life, or consume fruit from the tree of life, our glorified bodies will totally digest every bit of it, and have no elimination of waste.

Rev.22: 2 The leaves of the tree are "for the healing of the nations." The leaves of the tree of life seem to symbolize **perpetual healing** that God has provided for His saints on the new earth.

Since there is no sickness on the new earth, the leaves might be "preventive medicine".

Perhaps it's not that we couldn't get sick, but that by God's design and protection, sicknesses and debilitating accidents simply will not happen there.

Like in the Garden of Eden; it's not that Adam and Eve couldn't have gotten sick or hurt, but had they not sinned, they simply wouldn't have gotten sick or hurt.

The most amazing thing about the new eternal city is that **God's throne** and that of the Lamb will be **relocated** to the New Jerusalem so that God can live with His people.

Ezekiel 37: 27, 28 says: *My tabernacle also shall be with them: yea, I will be their God, and they shall be my people. And the heathen shall know that I the Lord do sanctify Israel, when my sanctuary shall be in the midst of them for evermore.* This long awaited prophecy that Satan tried so hard to foil, will finally be confirmed.

Rev. 22: 5 Even without the sun or moon, there will be no night there or need of artificial light. The glory of the Lord God gives them light. Evidently sleep will not be necessary for resurrected, immortal beings.

Children will **not** be born there. *Matt. 22:30* Jesus said "For in the resurrection they neither marry, nor are given in marriage, but are as the angels of God in heaven."

As the bride of Christ our total devotion will be to Jesus Christ our Savior. There will be no interest or desire to be married to anyone else who lives there.

Verse 5 also says: The resurrected saints will reign **on** the new earth forever, **but** over whom, or what will they reign?

Apparently, the saints will reign over the ***new earth*** its self to subdue it and maintain it, much like Adam and Eve were instructed to do. *Gen.1:28*

Since there are many languages spoken on earth, one might wonder how many languages will be spoken in heaven. Probably only one and it will most likely be Hebrew; based on *Acts 26:12-14.*

On the Damascus road Paul heard *a voice from heaven say to him in the* **Hebrew** *tongue,* "Saul, Saul, why persecutest thou me? It is hard for thee to kick against the pricks."

The new earth will have abundant life (including tame animals) and will need continuous maintenance. His servants will be delighted to do whatever is necessary to keep the new earth productive and beautiful. Fatigue and weariness will not be an issue there.

Rev.19:14 speaks of horses in heaven; it says: the armies which were in heaven followed Him upon white horses, clothed in fine linen, white and clean.

Since heaven will be an extension of the millennial reign of Christ we can probably include the tame animals spoken of in *Isaiah 11: 6-9*

Isaiah 11: 6-9 (Paraphrased) The wolf shall dwell with the lamb, and the leopard shall lie down with the kid; and the calf and the young lion together; and a little child shall lead them. The cow and the bear shall feed; their young ones shall lie down together: and the lion shall eat straw like the ox. The sucking child shall play on the hole of the asp. They shall not hurt or destroy in all my holy mountain: the earth shall be full of the knowledge of the Lord, as the waters cover the sea.

Rev. 22: 8, 9 Again, John is so overwhelmed that he mistakenly falls down before the feet of the angel to worship. Again the angel immediately tells him, **"Do not do it!**

I am a fellow servant; ...**Worship God!"** (John made the same mistake in Ch.19:10)

John has made a huge mistake in worshipping anyone other than God. He has broken the First Commandment, not once but twice, and yet **God knows** John's faithful heart, and **understands** that John was simply overwhelmed by all that he has seen.

REVELATION   Chapter 22 B   Even So, Come, Lord Jesus

Isn't it nice to know that God knows our faithful heart and He understands our human weaknesses when life is overwhelming.

Rev. 22:11 In the last days there will come a time when it will be too late to repent. Repentance will no longer be an option. Any decisions made to accept or reject Jesus will be fixed forever. All that remains are rewards and consequences. As spiritual beings we will always exist somewhere; either heaven or hell.

For those who trust and obey there will be complete access to the tree of life and full freedom to enter and leave and return to the magnificent eternal city of God. Jesus is the bright, morning star (the new beginning) in whom we place our eternal hope.

Rev. 22:18, A very stern warning is given to anyone who would attempt to alter the word of God with the intention of changing its' prophetic message. God will **add** to them the plagues that are written in this book.

Rev. 22:19 If anyone attempts to **take away** from the words of this book anything that would change its' *prophetic message*, he will be denied access to the book of life, the holy city, and the promises, and blessings that are written in this book.

That doesn't mean that there shouldn't be different versions of the bible, but none of them should change the prophetic message of God's word.

Rev. 22:20 John hears Jesus' final reminder as He says "Surely I come quickly."

John might be recounting all that he has seen and heard in this awesome prophetic vision of things that must be hereafter *(Rev.4:1)* and yet his response is a robust welcome as he declares, **"Even so, come Lord Jesus."**

Rev. 22:21 The final benediction (blessing) is this:

"The grace of our Lord Jesus Christ be with you all. Amen."

CPSIA information can be obtained at www.ICGtesting.com
Printed in the USA
BVOW041219270812

298811BV00002B/2/P